# Modern Biology®

## Quizzes
## with Answer Key

**HOLT, RINEHART AND WINSTON**

A Harcourt Education Company

Orlando • Austin • New York • San Diego • Toronto • London

ISBN 0-03-036721-2

21 22 060 19 18

450747780

ISBN 0-03-036721-2

21 22  0607  19 18

4500747790

# CONTENTS

Name _____ Class _____ Date _____

# The Science of Life

**In the space provided, write the letter of the description that best matches the term or phrase.**

_____ **1.** genes

_____ **2.** ecology

_____ **3.** scientific method

_____ **4.** theory

_____ **5.** magnification

**a.** organized approach to science

**b.** set of confirmed hypotheses

**c.** study of interactions of organisms with each other and their environment

**d.** increase of an object's apparent size

**e.** contain the instructions for traits

**In the space provided, write the letter of the term or phrase that best completes each statement or best answers each question.**

_____ **6.** The study of life is called
    **a.** ecology.
    **b.** biology.
    **c.** morphology.
    **d.** phylogeny.

_____ **7.** Which of the following is NOT one of the seven characteristics of life?
    **a.** growth and development
    **b.** responsiveness
    **c.** specific shape or structure
    **d.** reproduction

_____ **8.** Organisms have been classified into three major subdivisions called
    **a.** domains.
    **b.** kingdoms.
    **c.** species.
    **d.** groups.

_____ **9.** All of the following are good rules of lab safety EXCEPT
    **a.** wearing safety goggles.
    **b.** working alone in the lab when you must make up an assigned experiment.
    **c.** never working in the lab without supervision.
    **d.** asking for permission to use equipment.

_____ **10.** The process by which organisms with favorable traits are more likely to survive and reproduce is called
    **a.** evolution.
    **b.** reproduction.
    **c.** genetic mutation.
    **d.** natural selection.

Assessment

# The Science of Life

In the space provided, write the letter of the description that best matches the term or phrase.

_____ 1. genes

_____ 2. ecology

_____ 3. scientific method

_____ 4. theory

_____ 5. magnification

a. organized approach to science

b. set of confirmed hypotheses

c. study of interactions of organisms with each other and their environment

d. increase of an object's apparent size

e. contain the instructions for traits

In the space provided, write the letter of the term or phrase that best completes each statement or best answers each question.

_____ 6. The study of life is called
a. ecology.
b. biology.
c. morphology.
d. phylogeny.

_____ 7. Which of the following is NOT one of the seven characteristics of life?
a. growth and development
b. responsiveness
c. specific shape or structure
d. reproduction

_____ 8. Organisms have been classified into three major subdivisions called
a. domains.
b. kingdoms.
c. species.
d. groups.

_____ 9. All of the following are good rules of lab safety EXCEPT
a. wearing safety goggles.
b. working alone in the lab when you must make up an assigned experiment.
c. never working in the lab without supervision.
d. asking for permission to use equipment.

_____ 10. The process by which organisms with favorable traits are more likely to survive and reproduce is called
a. evolution.
b. reproduction.
c. genetic mutation.
d. natural selection.

Name _____ Class _____ Date _____

# Chemistry of Life

**In the space provided, write the letter of the term or phrase that best completes each statement or best answers each question.**
**Questions 1–4 refer to the figure at right.**

_____ **1.** This figure represents a model of a(n)
   **a.** molecule.
   **b.** atom.
   **c.** compound.
   **d.** ion.

_____ **2.** The structure labeled *A* represents
   **a.** a proton.
   **b.** a neutron.
   **c.** the electron cloud.
   **d.** the nucleus.

_____ **3.** The structure labeled *B* represents
   **a.** an atom.                **c.** the electron cloud.
   **b.** an ion.                 **d.** the nucleus.

_____ **4.** The structures labeled *C* and *D* represent
   **a.** a proton and a neutron.
   **b.** a neutron and an electron.
   **c.** a proton and an electron.
   **d.** one positive and one negative electron.

_____ **5.** The speed of a chemical reaction is increased by
   **a.** an enzyme.             **c.** glucose.
   **b.** the reactant.          **d.** a buffer.

_____ **6.** Atoms or molecules move least rapidly in a
   **a.** gas.                   **c.** liquid.
   **b.** solid.                 **d.** solution.

**In the space provided, write the letter of the description that best matches the term or phrase.**

_____ **7.** neutral                **a.** a mixture in which all substances are evenly distributed

_____ **8.** solution               **b.** allows a needle to float on water

_____ **9.** ionic compounds        **c.** dissolve best in water

_____ **10.** surface tension        **d.** equal numbers of hydronium and hydroxide ions

Name _____ Class _____ Date _____

Assessment

# Chemistry of Life

In the space provided, write the letter of the term or phrase that best completes
each statement or best answers each question.
Questions 1–4 refer to the figure at right.

_____ 1. This figure represents a model of a(n)
   a. molecule.
   b. atom.
   c. compound.
   d. ion.

_____ 2. The structure labeled A
   represents
   a. a proton.
   b. a neutron.
   c. the electron cloud.
   d. the nucleus.

_____ 3. The structure labeled B represents
   a. an atom.          c. the electron cloud
   b. an ion.           d. the nucleus.

_____ 4. The structures labeled C and D represent
   a. a proton and a neutron.
   b. a neutron and an electron.
   c. a proton and an electron.
   d. one positive and one negative electron.

_____ 5. The speed of a chemical reaction is increased by
   a. an enzyme.        c. glucose.
   b. the reactant.     d. a buffer.

_____ 6. Atoms or molecules move least rapidly in a
   a. gas.              c. liquid.
   b. solid.            d. solution.

In the space provided, write the letter of the description that best matches the
term or phrase.

_____ 7. neutral          a. a mixture in which all substances are
                             evenly distributed
_____ 8. solution         b. allows a needle to float on water
_____ 9. ionic compounds  c. dissolve best in water
_____ 10. surface tension d. equal numbers of hydronium and
                             hydroxide ions

Copyright © by Holt, Rinehart and Winston. All rights reserved.

Modern Biology                    8                    Quiz

Name _____ Class _____ Date _____

# Biochemistry

**In the space provided, write the letter of the description that best matches the term or phrase.**

_____1. saturated fatty acid

_____2. nucleic acid

_____3. polysaccharides

_____4. amino acids

_____5. RNA

**a.** building blocks of proteins

**b.** hard at room temperature

**c.** a molecular chain of nucleotides

**d.** starch, cellulose, and glycogen

**e.** stores and transfers information from DNA

**In the space provided, write the letter of the term or phrase that best completes each statement or best answers each question.**

_____ 6. DNA and RNA are made up of nucleotides, which contain
  **a.** a sugar, a base, and a phosphate group.
  **b.** a sugar, an acid, and a phosphate group.
  **c.** ATP, a base, and a phosphate group.
  **d.** amino acids.

_____ 7. Large, nonpolar organic molecules that include waxes and store more energy per gram than other organic compounds are
  **a.** nucleic acids.          **c.** lipids.
  **b.** carbohydrates.        **d.** proteins.

_____ 8. Unlike saturated fatty acids, unsaturated fatty acids contain what kind of bonds between carbon atoms?
  **a.** ionic                    **c.** single
  **b.** hydrogen              **d.** double

_____ 9. The main difference among different amino acids is in
  **a.** the kind of atom in the center of the molecule.
  **b.** the type of bonding involved.
  **c.** the number of bonds involved.
  **d.** their R groups.

_____10. Monomers link to form polymers through a chemical reaction called
  **a.** ATP.
  **b.** a hydrolysis reaction.
  **c.** a condensation reaction.
  **d.** None of the above

Assessment

# Biochemistry

In the space provided, write the letter of the description that best matches the term or phrase.

_____ 1. saturated fatty acid

_____ 2. nucleic acid

_____ 3. polysaccharides

_____ 4. amino acids

_____ 5. RNA

a. building blocks of proteins

b. hard at room temperature

c. a molecular chain of nucleotides

d. starch, cellulose, and glycogen

e. stores and transfers information from DNA

In the space provided, write the letter of the term or phrase that best completes each statement or best answers each question.

_____ 6. DNA and RNA are made up of nucleotides, which contain
   a. a sugar, a base, and a phosphate group.
   b. a sugar, an acid, and a phosphate group.
   c. ATP, a base, and a phosphate group.
   d. amino acids.

_____ 7. Large, nonpolar organic molecules that include waxes and store more energy per gram than other organic compounds are
   a. nucleic acids.          c. lipids.
   b. carbohydrates.          d. proteins.

_____ 8. Unlike saturated fatty acids, unsaturated fatty acids contain what kind of bonds between carbon atoms?
   a. ionic                   c. single
   b. hydrogen                d. double

_____ 9. The main difference among different amino acids is in
   a. the kind of atom in the center of the molecule.
   b. the type of bonding involved.
   c. the number of bonds involved.
   d. their R groups.

_____ 10. Monomers link to form polymers through a chemical reaction called
   a. ATP.
   b. a hydrolysis reaction.
   c. a condensation reaction.
   d. None of the above

Name _____ Class _____ Date _____

# Cell Structure and Function

**In the space provided, write the letter of the description that best matches the term or phrase.**

___g___ **1.** endoplasmic reticulum

___f___ **2.** central vacuole

___b___ **3.** chloroplasts

___c___ **4.** Golgi apparatus

___d___ **5.** lysosomes

___a___ **6.** mitochondrion

___e___ **7.** cell

**a.** an organelle that produces ATP

**b.** in plants, organelles that use light to make organic compounds

**c.** the cell's labeling and packaging center

**d.** small organelles that contain the cell's digestive enzymes

**e.** smallest unit of life

**f.** in plant cells, a large, membrane-bound sac that stores water, enzymes, or other substances

**g.** system of internal membranes that move proteins and other substances throughout the cell

**In the space provided, write the letter of the term or phrase that best completes each statement or best answers each question.**

___c___ **8.** Most functions of a eukaryotic cell are controlled by the cell's
    **a.** cell wall.
    **b.** ribosomes.
    **c.** nucleus.
    **d.** mitochondria.

___d___ **9.** Which of the following organelles is found only in plants?
    **a.** ribosomes
    **b.** nucleus
    **c.** mitochondria
    **d.** central vacuole

___b___ **10.** Smooth ER lacks
    **a.** nuclei.
    **b.** ribosomes.
    **c.** chloroplasts.
    **d.** lysosomes.

# Cell Structure and Function

**In the space provided, write the letter of the description that best matches the term or phrase.**

_____ 1. endoplasmic reticulum

_____ 2. central vacuole

_____ 3. chloroplasts

_____ 4. Golgi apparatus

_____ 5. lysosomes

_____ 6. mitochondrion

_____ 7. cell

a. an organelle that produces ATP

b. in plants, organelles that use light to make organic compounds

c. the cell's labeling and packaging center

d. small organelles that contain the cell's digestive enzymes

e. smallest unit of life

f. in plant cells, a large, membrane-bound sac that stores water, enzymes, or other substances

g. system of internal membranes that move proteins and other substances throughout the cell

**In the space provided, write the letter of the term or phrase that best completes each statement or best answers each question.**

_____ 8. Most functions of a eukaryotic cell are controlled by the cell's
   a. cell wall.
   b. ribosomes.
   c. nucleus.
   d. mitochondria.

_____ 9. Which of the following organelles is found only in plants?
   a. ribosomes
   b. nucleus
   c. mitochondria
   d. central vacuole

_____ 10. Smooth ER lacks
   a. nuclei.
   b. ribosomes.
   c. chloroplasts.
   d. lysosomes.

Assessment

# Homeostasis and Cell Transport

**In the space provided, write the letter of the description that best matches the term or phrase.**

_____ **1.** osmosis

_____ **2.** carrier protein

_____ **3.** active transport

_____ **4.** contractile vacuole

**a.** forces excess water out of a cell

**b.** transport of a substance against its concentration gradient

**c.** movement of a water down its concentration gradient

**d.** used to transport substances down their concentration gradient

**In the space provided, write the letter of the term or phrase that best completes each statement or best answers each question.**

_____ **5.** If a molecule's concentration outside a cell is higher than it is inside the cell, that solution is
    **a.** isotonic.
    **b.** hypertonic.
    **c.** hypotonic.
    **d.** None of the above

_____ **6.** If someone spills perfume in one room, people can soon smell it in a nearby room. Which of the following is this an example of?
    **a.** facilitated diffusion
    **b.** osmosis
    **c.** diffusion
    **d.** active transport

_____ **7.** Molecules that can diffuse across the membrane include
    **a.** many polar molecules.
    **b.** many nonpolar molecules.
    **c.** sugars
    **d.** amino acids.

_____ **8.** Which of the following is an example of active transport?
    **a.** equilibrium
    **b.** sodium-potassium pump
    **c.** facilitated diffusion
    **d.** osmosis

_____ **9.** The sodium-potassium pump transports
    **a.** sodium ions out of the cell.
    **b.** sodium ions into the cell.
    **c.** potassium ions out of the cell.
    **d.** Both (b) and (c)

_____ **10.** Which of the following substances are too large for carrier proteins?
    **a.** ions
    **b.** glucose
    **c.** polysaccharides
    **d.** None of the above

Assessment

# Homeostasis and Cell Transport

**In the space provided, write the letter of the description that best matches the term or phrase.**

_____ 1. osmosis

_____ 2. carrier protein

_____ 3. active transport

_____ 4. contractile vacuole

a. forces excess water out of a cell

b. transport of a substance against its concentration gradient

c. movement of a water down its concentration gradient

d. used to transport substances down their concentration gradient

**In the space provided, write the letter of the term or phrase that best completes each statement or best answers each question.**

_____ 5. If a molecule's concentration outside a cell is higher than it is inside the cell, that solution is
    a. isotonic.
    b. hypertonic.
    c. hypotonic.
    d. None of the above

_____ 6. If someone spills perfume in one room, people can soon smell it in a nearby room. Which of the following is this an example of?
    a. facilitated diffusion
    b. osmosis
    c. diffusion
    d. active transport

_____ 7. Molecules that can diffuse across the membrane include
    a. many polar molecules.
    b. many nonpolar molecules.
    c. sugars.
    d. amino acids.

_____ 8. Which of the following is an example of active transport?
    a. equilibrium
    b. sodium-potassium pump
    c. facilitated diffusion
    d. osmosis

_____ 9. The sodium-potassium pump transports
    a. sodium ions out of the cell.
    b. sodium ions into the cell.
    c. potassium ions out of the cell.
    d. Both (b) and (c)

_____ 10. Which of the following substances are too large for carrier proteins?
    a. ions
    b. glucose
    c. polysaccharides
    d. None of the above

Name _____ Class _____ Date _____

# Photosynthesis

**In the space provided, write the letter of the stage that best matches the phrase. Answers may be used more than once.**

_____ **1.** Light energy is stored as ATP and NADPH.

_____ **2.** Organic compounds are formed using carbon dioxide.

_____ **3.** Calvin cycle

_____ **4.** Excited electrons are passed along an electron transport chain.

_____ **5.** Pigment molecules absorb energy.

_____ **6.** Water is split.

**a.** Stage 1 of photosynthesis

**b.** Stage 2 of photosynthesis

**In the space provided, write the letter of the term or phrase that best completes each statement or best answers each question.**

_____ **7.** Yellow and orange plant pigments are known as which of the following?
  **a.** chlorophyll
  **b.** electron transport chains
  **c.** carotenoids
  **d.** thylakoids

_____ **8.** The rate of photosynthesis decreases as the
  **a.** oxygen concentration decreases.
  **b.** carbon dioxide concentration decreases.
  **c.** light intensity increases.
  **d.** All of the above

_____ **9.** In the first stage of photosynthesis, hydrogen ions are pumped
  **a.** into a photosystem.
  **b.** out of the chloroplast.
  **c.** into the thylakoids.
  **d.** Both (a) and (b)

_____ **10.** Products of the Calvin cycle are
  **a.** three-carbon sugars.
  **b.** used to produce organic compounds.
  **c.** used to regenerate the initial five-carbon compound.
  **d.** All of the above

Assessment

# Photosynthesis

In the space provided, write the letter of the stage that best matches the phrase. Answers may be used more than once.

_____ 1. Light energy is stored as ATP and NADPH.

_____ 2. Organic compounds are formed using carbon dioxide.

_____ 3. Calvin cycle

_____ 4. Excited electrons are passed along an electron transport chain.

_____ 5. Pigment molecules absorb energy

_____ 6. Water is split.

a. Stage 1 of photosynthesis
b. Stage 2 of photosynthesis

In the space provided, write the letter of the term or phrase that best completes each statement or best answers each question.

_____ 7. Yellow and orange plant pigments are known as which of the following?
a. chlorophyll                          c. carotenoids
b. electron transport chains      d. thylakoids

_____ 8. The rate of photosynthesis decreases as the
a. oxygen concentration decreases.
b. carbon dioxide concentration decreases.
c. light intensity increases.
d. All of the above

_____ 9. In the first stage of photosynthesis, hydrogen ions are pumped
a. into a photosystem.
b. out of the chloroplast.
c. into the thylakoids.
d. Both (a) and (b)

_____ 10. Products of the Calvin cycle are
a. three-carbon sugars.
b. used to produce organic compounds.
c. used to regenerate the initial five-carbon compound.
d. All of the above

Name _____ Class _____ Date _____

# Cellular Respiration

**In the space provided, write the letter of the description that best matches the term or phrase.**

_____ **1.** lactic acid fermentation

_____ **2.** alcoholic fermentation

_____ **3.** electron transport chain

_____ **4.** Krebs cycle

_____ **5.** $NAD^+$

**a.** occurs in the inner membrane of the mitochondrion

**b.** recycled during fermentation

**c.** sore muscles

**d.** rising bread dough

**e.** results in the formation of NADH and $FADH_2$

**In the space provided, write the letter of the term or phrase that best completes each statement or best answers each question.**

_____ **6.** Glucose is converted into pyruvic acid during
  **a.** glycolysis.
  **b.** the Krebs cycle.
  **c.** fermentation.
  **d.** carbon fixation.

_____ **7.** Some of the glucose required for cellular respiration in humans is obtained by
  **a.** making food.
  **b.** taking vitamins.
  **c.** eating food.
  **d.** All of the above

_____ **8.** If oxygen is NOT available to accept electrons during aerobic respiration,
  **a.** aerobic processes stop.
  **b.** fermentation proceeds.
  **c.** only small amounts of ATP can be produced.
  **d.** All of the above

_____ **9.** During the second stage of cellular respiration,
  **a.** there is a net gain of two ATP.
  **b.** the electron transport chain and chemiosmosis use the energy in NADH and $FADH_2$ to produce up to 34 ATP.
  **c.** energy is transferred from glucose and pyruvic acid to NADH and $FADH_2$.
  **d.** Both (b) and (c)

**Question 10 refers to the chemical equation below.**

$$C_6H_{12}O_6 + 6O_2 \xrightarrow{\text{enzymes}} 6CO_2 + 6H_2O + \text{energy}$$

_____ **10.** The equation summarizes the overall process of
  **a.** the Krebs cycle.
  **b.** photosynthesis.
  **c.** cellular respiration.
  **d.** fermentation.

Assessment

# Cellular Respiration

**In the space provided, write the letter of the description that best matches the term or phrase.**

_____ 1. lactic acid fermentation

_____ 2. alcoholic fermentation

_____ 3. electron transport chain

_____ 4. Krebs cycle

_____ 5. NAD$^+$

a. occurs in the inner membrane of the mitochondrion

b. recycled during fermentation

c. sore muscles

d. rising bread dough

e. results in the formation of NADH and FADH$_2$

**In the space provided, write the letter of the term or phrase that best completes each statement or best answers each question.**

_____ 6. Glucose is converted into pyruvic acid during
    a. glycolysis.
    b. the Krebs cycle.
    c. fermentation.
    d. carbon fixation.

_____ 7. Some of the glucose required for cellular respiration in humans is obtained by
    a. making food.
    b. taking vitamins.
    c. eating food.
    d. All of the above

_____ 8. If oxygen is NOT available to accept electrons during aerobic respiration,
    a. aerobic processes stop.
    b. fermentation proceeds.
    c. only small amounts of ATP can be produced.
    d. All of the above

_____ 9. During the second stage of cellular respiration,
    a. there is a net gain of two ATP.
    b. the electron transport chain and chemiosmosis use the energy in NADH and FADH$_2$ to produce up to 34 ATP.
    c. energy is transferred from glucose and pyruvic acid to NADH and FADH$_2$.
    d. Both (b) and (c)

**Question 10 refers to the chemical equation below.**

$$C_6H_{12}O_6 + 6O_2 \xrightarrow{\text{enzymes}} 6CO_2 + 6H_2O + \text{energy}$$

_____ 10. The equation summarizes the overall process of
    a. the Krebs cycle.
    b. photosynthesis.
    c. cellular respiration.
    d. fermentation.

Name _____ Class _____ Date _____

# Cell Reproduction

**In the space provided, write the letter of the description that best matches the term or phrase.**

_____ **1.** cytokinesis

_____ **2.** cell cycle

_____ **3.** meiosis

_____ **4.** synthesis (S) phase

_____ **5.** centromere

**a.** DNA is copied

**b.** formation of gametes

**c.** holds two chromatids together

**d.** cytoplasm divides

**e.** a repeating sequence of cellular growth and division

**In the space provided, write the letter of the term or phrase that best completes each statement or best answers each question.**

_____ **6.** In human sexual reproduction, a male haploid gamete and a female haploid gamete unite to form which of the following?
   **a.** an egg cell with 46 chromosomes
   **b.** a zygote with 23 chromosomes
   **c.** a zygote with 46 chromosomes
   **d.** a sperm cell with 23 chromosomes

_____ **7.** Chromosomes that determine the sex of an individual are called
   **a.** autosomes.
   **b.** sex chromosomes.
   **c.** homologous chromosomes.
   **d.** chromatids.

_____ **8.** Chromosomes that are similar in size, shape, and genetic content are called
   **a.** autosomes.
   **b.** sex chromosomes.
   **c.** homologous chromosomes.
   **d.** chromatids.

_____ **9.** Mitosis occurs
   **a.** immediately after the synthesis phase.
   **b.** before the second growth phase.
   **c.** after the second growth phase.
   **d.** after cytokinesis.

_____ **10.** DNA replication is checked during the
   **a.** cell growth ($G_1$) checkpoint.
   **b.** DNA synthesis ($G_2$) checkpoint.
   **c.** mitosis checkpoint.
   **d.** cytokinesis checkpoint.

Assessment

# Cell Reproduction

**In the space provided, write the letter of the description that best matches the term or phrase.**

_____ 1. cytokinesis

_____ 2. cell cycle

_____ 3. meiosis

_____ 4. synthesis (S) phase

_____ 5. centromere

a. DNA is copied

b. formation of gametes

c. holds two chromatids together

d. cytoplasm divides

e. a repeating sequence of cellular growth and division

**In the space provided, write the letter of the term or phrase that best completes each statement or best answers each question.**

_____ 6. In human sexual reproduction, a male haploid gamete and a female haploid gamete unite to form which of the following?
a. an egg cell with 46 chromosomes
b. a zygote with 23 chromosomes
c. a zygote with 46 chromosomes
d. a sperm cell with 23 chromosomes

_____ 7. Chromosomes that determine the sex of an individual are called
a. autosomes.
b. sex chromosomes.
c. homologous chromosomes.
d. chromatids.

_____ 8. Chromosomes that are similar in size, shape, and genetic content are called
a. autosomes.
b. sex chromosomes.
c. homologous chromosomes.
d. chromatids.

_____ 9. Mitosis occurs
a. immediately after the synthesis phase.
b. before the second growth phase.
c. after the second growth phase.
d. after cytokinesis.

_____ 10. DNA replication is checked during the
a. cell growth (G1) checkpoint.
b. DNA synthesis (G2) checkpoint.
c. mitosis checkpoint.
d. cytokinesis checkpoint.

Name _____  Class _____  Date _____

# Fundamentals of Genetics

**In the space provided, write the letter of the description that best matches the term or phrase.**

_____ **1.** 1 *WW* : 2 *Ww* : 1 *ww*

_____ **2.** Punnett square

_____ **3.** test cross

_____ **4.** probability

_____ **5.** all *Ww* offspring

_____ **6.** alleles

**a.** result of a cross between the parents *WW* and *ww*

**b.** result from a cross between the parents *Ww* and *Ww*

**c.** likelihood that an event will occur

**d.** used to determine the genotype of a purple-flowering pea plant

**e.** diagram used to predict the outcome of a genetic cross

**f.** Mendel's factors

**In the space provided, write the letter of the term or phrase that best completes each statement or best answers each question.**

_____ **7.** A series of genetic crosses results in 787 long-stemmed plants and 277 short-stemmed plants. The probability that you will obtain short-stemmed plants if you repeat this experiment is

    **a.** $\dfrac{277}{1,064}$.
        **c.** $\dfrac{787}{277}$.

    **b.** $\dfrac{277}{787}$.
        **d.** $\dfrac{787}{1,064}$.

_____ **8.** Which of the following is an example of a test cross?
    **a.** *YY* × *YY*
        **c.** *Yy* × *Yy*
    **b.** *YY* × *yy*
        **d.** All of the above

**Refer to the figure at right, which represents a monohybrid cross between two individuals that are heterozygous for a trait, to answer questions 9 and 10 .**

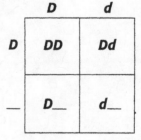

_____ **9.** If the resulting phenotypic ratio is 3:1, the missing parental allele is
    **a.** *d.*
        **c.** *Dd.*
    **b.** *D.*
        **d.** *DD.*

_____ **10.** The two unknown genotypes in the offspring are
    **a.** *DD* and *dd.*
        **c.** *dd* and *DD.*
    **b.** *Dd* and *Dd.*
        **d.** *Dd* and *dd.*

Assessment

# Fundamentals of Genetics

In the space provided, write the letter of the description that best matches the term or phrase.

_____ 1. 1 WW : 2 Ww : 1 ww

_____ 2. Punnett square

_____ 3. test cross

_____ 4. probability

_____ 5. all Ww offspring

_____ 6. alleles

a. result of a cross between the parents WW and ww

b. result from a cross between the parents Ww and Ww

c. likelihood that an event will occur

d. used to determine the genotype of a purple-flowering pea plant

e. diagram used to predict the outcome of a genetic cross

f. Mendel's factors

In the space provided, write the letter of the term or phrase that best completes each statement or best answers each question.

_____ 7. A series of genetic crosses results in 787 long-stemmed plants and 277 short-stemmed plants. The probability that you will obtain short-stemmed plants if you repeat this experiment is

a. $\frac{277}{1,064}$

b. $\frac{277}{787}$

c. $\frac{787}{277}$

d. $\frac{787}{1,064}$

_____ 8. Which of the following is an example of a test cross?

a. YY × YY

b. YY × yy

c. Yy × Yy

d. All of the above

Refer to the figure at right, which represents a monohybrid cross between two individuals that are heterozygous for a trait, to answer questions 9 and 10.

|   | D | d |
|---|---|---|
| D | DD | Dd |
| d | D_ | _d |

_____ 9. If the resulting phenotypic ratio is 3:1, the missing parental allele is

a. d.

b. D.

c. Dd.

d. DD.

_____ 10. The two unknown genotypes in the offspring are

a. DD and dd.

b. Dd and Dd.

c. dd and DD.

d. Dd and dd.

Name _____ Class _____ Date _____

Assessment

# DNA, RNA, and Protein Synthesis

**In the space provided, write the letter of the term or phrase that best completes each statement or best answers each question.**

_____ 1. Each nucleotide in a DNA molecule consists of a
   **a.** sulfur group, a five-carbon sugar molecule, and a nitrogen base.
   **b.** phosphate group, a six-carbon sugar molecule, and a nitrogen base.
   **c.** phosphate group, a five-carbon sugar molecule, and an oxygen base.
   **d.** phosphate group, a five-carbon sugar molecule, and a nitrogen base.

_____ 2. Which of the following describes the base-pairing rules in DNA?
   **a.** Purines pair only with purines.
   **b.** Pyrimidines pair only with pyrimidines.
   **c.** Adenine pairs with guanine, and thymine pairs with cytosine.
   **d.** Adenine pairs with thymine, and cytosine pairs with guanine.

_____ 3. In 1952, Hershey and Chase used a bacteriophage to determine that genetic material is made of which of the following?
   **a.** protein                    **c.** DNA
   **b.** RNA                         **d.** $^{35}$S

_____ 4. The areas where DNA separates during replication are called
   **a.** helicases.                  **c.** replication forks.
   **b.** polymerases.                **d.** proofreaders.

_____ 5. Which of the following proofreads the new DNA molecules during replication?
   **a.** DNA polymerases             **c.** DNA helicases
   **b.** replication forks           **d.** the original strand of DNA

**In the space provided, write the letter of the description that best matches the term or phrase.**

_____ 6. transcription          **a.** sequence of three bases in mRNA

_____ 7. translation            **b.** mRNA to protein

_____ 8. codon                  **c.** complete genetic content of an organism

_____ 9. anticodon              **d.** sequence of three bases in tRNA

_____ 10. genome                **e.** DNA to mRNA

Assessment

# DNA, RNA, and Protein Synthesis

**In the space provided, write the letter of the term or phrase that best completes each statement or best answers each question.**

_____ 1. Each nucleotide in a DNA molecule consists of a
   a. sulfur group, a five-carbon sugar molecule, and a nitrogen base.
   b. phosphate group, a six-carbon sugar molecule, and a nitrogen base.
   c. phosphate group, a five-carbon sugar molecule, and an oxygen base.
   d. phosphate group, a five-carbon sugar molecule, and a nitrogen base.

_____ 2. Which of the following describes the base-pairing rules in DNA?
   a. Purines pair only with purines.
   b. Pyrimidines pair only with pyrimidines.
   c. Adenine pairs with guanine, and thymine pairs with cytosine.
   d. Adenine pairs with thymine, and cytosine pairs with guanine.

_____ 3. In 1952, Hershey and Chase used a bacteriophage to determine that
   genetic material is made of which of the following?
   a. protein              c. DNA
   b. RNA                  d. ss

_____ 4. The areas where DNA separates during replication are called
   a. helicases.           c. replication forks.
   b. polymerases.         d. proofreaders.

_____ 5. Which of the following proofreads the new DNA molecules during
   replication?
   a. DNA polymerases      c. DNA helicases
   b. replication forks    d. the original strand of DNA

**In the space provided, write the letter of the description that best matches the term or phrase.**

_____ 6. transcription       a. sequence of three bases in mRNA

_____ 7. translation         b. mRNA to protein

_____ 8. codon               c. complete genetic content of an
                                organism

_____ 9. anticodon           d. sequence of three bases in tRNA

_____ 10. genome             e. DNA to mRNA

Assessment

# Gene Expression

**In the space provided, write the letter of the term or phrase that best completes each statement or best answers each question.**

_____ 1. Regulating gene expression is necessary in living organisms
   **a.** so that the repressor will never bind to the operator.
   **b.** to allow RNA polymerase continuous access to genes.
   **c.** to avoid wasting their energy and resources on producing proteins that are not needed or are already available.
   **d.** to ensure that the operon is always in the "on" mode.

_____ 2. The *lac* operon enables a bacterium to build the proteins needed for lactose metabolism only when
   **a.** glucose is present.          **c.** galactose is present.
   **b.** tryptophan is present.        **d.** lactose is present.

_____ 3. Which of the following is NOT true about the regulation of gene expression in eukaryotic cells?
   **a.** Regulation of gene expression in eukaryotes is more complex than in prokaryotes.
   **b.** Operons play a major role in regulation of eukaryote gene expression.
   **c.** Regulation of gene expression can occur before, during, or after transcription.
   **d.** Regulation of gene expression can occur in euchromatin.

_____ 4. A DNA chip is used to determine
   **a.** which genes are being expressed.
   **b.** where an operon is located.
   **c.** when a tumor forms.
   **d.** the location of a homeobox.

_____ 5. The *lac* operon turns "off" when
   **a.** glucose is absent.            **c.** RNA polymerase is absent.
   **b.** lactose is absent.            **d.** lactose is present.

**In the space provided, write the letter of the description that best matches the term or phrase.**

_____ 6. intron
_____ 7. oncogene
_____ 8. exon
_____ 9. repressor protein
_____ 10. enhancer

   **a.** long segments of eukaryotic DNA that have no coding information
   **b.** gene that causes uncontrolled cell proliferation
   **c.** sequence of DNA that can be bound to a transcription factor
   **d.** can bind to an operator, which stops transcription
   **e.** portions of a eukaryotic gene that are translated

# Gene Expression

**In the space provided, write the letter of the term or phrase that best completes each statement or best answers each question.**

_____ 1. Regulating gene expression is necessary in living organisms
   a. so that the repressor will never bind to the operator.
   b. to allow RNA polymerase continuous access to genes.
   c. to avoid wasting their energy and resources on producing proteins that are not needed or are already available.
   d. to ensure that the operon is always in the "on" mode.

_____ 2. The lac operon enables a bacterium to build the proteins needed for lactose metabolism only when
   a. glucose is present.          c. galactose is present.
   b. tryptophan is present.       d. lactose is present.

_____ 3. Which of the following is NOT true about the regulation of gene expression in eukaryotic cells?
   a. Regulation of gene expression in eukaryotes is more complex than in prokaryotes.
   b. Operons play a major role in regulation of eukaryote gene expression.
   c. Regulation of gene expression can occur before, during, or after transcription.
   d. Regulation of gene expression can occur in euchromatin.

_____ 4. A DNA chip is used to determine
   a. which genes are being expressed.
   b. where an operon is located.
   c. when a tumor forms.
   d. the location of a homeobox.

_____ 5. The lac operon turns "off" when
   a. glucose is absent.          c. RNA polymerase is absent.
   b. lactose is present.         d. lactose is absent.

**In the space provided, write the letter of the description that best matches the term or phrase.**

_____ 6. intron

_____ 7. oncogene

_____ 8. exon

_____ 9. repressor protein

_____ 10. enhancer

a. long segments of eukaryotic DNA that have no coding information

b. gene that causes uncontrolled cell proliferation

c. sequence of DNA that can be bound to a transcription factor

d. can bind to an operator, which stops transcription

e. portions of a eukaryotic gene that are translated

Assessment

# Inheritance Patterns and Human Genetics

**In the space provided, write the letter of the term or phrase that best completes each statement or best answers each question.**

_____ 1. When several genes influence a trait, the trait is said to be
    **a.** polygenic.
    **c.** codominant.
    **b.** incompletely dominant.
    **d.** completely dominant.

_____ 2. Which of the following genetic disorders is caused by an autosomal dominant allele?
    **a.** sickle cell anemia
    **c.** hemophilia
    **b.** Huntington's disease
    **d.** Tay-Sachs disease

_____ 3. The sex of an offspring is determined by the
    **a.** mother only.
    **c.** offspring only.
    **b.** both mother and father.
    **d.** father only.

_____ 4. Which type of mutation is likely to cause the least harm in an individual?
    **a.** frameshift mutation
    **c.** substitution
    **b.** deletion
    **d.** addition

**In the space provided, write the letter of the description that best matches the term or phrase.**

_____ 5. sickle cell anemia

_____ 6. breast cancer

_____ 7. gene therapy

_____ 8. genetic counseling

_____ 9. mutation

_____ 10. multiple alleles

**a.** determine the different ABO blood types

**b.** caused by a mutated allele that causes red blood cells to change shape

**c.** caused by a dominant allele located on an autosome

**d.** changes in DNA that can cause genetic disorders

**e.** informing people about genetic problems they or their offspring might have

**f.** replacing defective genes with copies of healthy genes, using gene technology

Assessment

# Inheritance Patterns and Human Genetics

**In the space provided, write the letter of the term or phrase that best completes each statement or best answers each question.**

_____ 1. When several genes influence a trait, the trait is said to be
        a. polygenic.               c. codominant.
        b. incompletely dominant.     d. completely dominant.

_____ 2. Which of the following genetic disorders is caused by an autosomal dominant allele?
        a. sickle cell anemia        c. hemophilia
        b. Huntington's disease    d. Tay-Sachs disease

_____ 3. The sex of an offspring is determined by the
        a. mother only.            c. offspring only.
        b. both mother and father.   d. father only.

_____ 4. Which type of mutation is likely to cause the least harm in an individual?
        a. frameshift mutation     c. substitution
        b. deletion                 d. addition

**In the space provided, write the letter of the description that best matches the term or phrase.**

_____ 5. sickle cell anemia

_____ 6. breast cancer

_____ 7. gene therapy

_____ 8. genetic counseling

_____ 9. mutation

_____ 10. multiple alleles

a. determine the different ABO blood types

b. caused by a mutated allele that causes red blood cells to change shape

c. caused by a dominant allele located on an autosome

d. changes in DNA that can cause genetic disorders

e. informing people about genetic problems they or their offspring might have

f. replacing defective genes with copies of healthy genes, using gene technology

# Gene Technology

**In the space provided, write the letter of the description that best matches the term or phrase.**

_____ **1.** genetic engineering

_____ **2.** vector

_____ **3.** plasmid

_____ **4.** cloning

_____ **5.** recombinant DNA

_____ **6.** restriction enzymes

_____ **7.** gel electrophoresis

**a.** made from DNA from two separate organisms

**b.** uses an electrical field to separate molecules

**c.** growing a large number of genetically identical cells from a single cell

**d.** alters an organism's DNA so it codes for new substances

**e.** can carry a DNA fragment into another cell

**f.** can be used as a vector

**g.** used to cut DNA at specific sequences

**In the space provided, write the letter of the term or phrase that best completes each statement or best answers each question.**

_____ **8.** Radioactive or fluorescent-labeled RNA or single-stranded DNA pieces that are complementary to the gene of interest and are used to confirm the presence of a cloned gene are called
   **a.** probes.
   **b.** plasmids.
   **c.** vaccines.
   **d.** clones.

_____ **9.** Plasmids
   **a.** are circular pieces of bacterial DNA.
   **b.** can replicate independently of the organism's main chromosome.
   **c.** are often used as vectors in genetic engineering experiments.
   **d.** All of the above

_____ **10.** To make a DNA fingerprint, which of the following is NOT required?
   **a.** forensics
   **b.** gel electrophoresis
   **c.** radioactive probes
   **d.** X-ray film

Assessment

# Gene Technology

In the space provided, write the letter of the description that best matches the term or phrase.

_____ 1. genetic engineering

_____ 2. vector

_____ 3. plasmid

_____ 4. cloning

_____ 5. recombinant DNA

_____ 6. restriction enzymes

_____ 7. gel electrophoresis

a. made from DNA from two separate organisms

b. uses an electrical field to separate molecules

c. growing a large number of genetically identical cells from a single cell

d. alters an organism's DNA so it codes for new substances

e. can carry a DNA fragment into another cell

f. can be used as a vector

g. used to cut DNA at specific sequences

In the space provided, write the letter of the term or phrase that best completes each statement or best answers each question.

_____ 8. Radioactive or fluorescent-labeled RNA or single-stranded DNA pieces that are complementary to the gene of interest and are used to confirm the presence of a cloned gene are called
   a. probes.
   b. plasmids.
   c. vaccines.
   d. clones.

_____ 9. Plasmids
   a. are circular pieces of bacterial DNA.
   b. can replicate independently of the organism's main chromosome.
   c. are often used as vectors in genetic engineering experiments.
   d. All of the above

_____ 10. To make a DNA fingerprint, which of the following is NOT required?
   a. forensics
   b. gel electrophoresis
   c. radioactive probes
   d. X-ray film

Assessment

# History of Life

**In the space provided, write the letter of the term or phrase that best completes each statement or best answers each question.**

_____ 1. What principle states that living things come from other living things?
  **a.** biogenesis
  **b.** spontaneous generation
  **c.** endosymbiosis
  **d.** chemosynthesis

_____ 2. Which mixture of gases is thought to have made up Earth's early atmosphere?
  **a.** nitrogen, hydrogen, water vapor, ammonia, methane
  **b.** carbon dioxide, nitrogen, oxygen, argon, ozone
  **c.** ozone, water vapor, carbon dioxide, ammonia
  **d.** methane, oxygen, hydrogen, argon, water vapor

_____ 3. Most scientists agree that the basic molecules of life could have formed spontaneously through simple chemistry on the early Earth. Which of the following was made by Miller and Urey in the laboratory?
  **a.** ozone
  **b.** DNA
  **c.** amino acids
  **d.** None of the above

_____ 4. Microspheres could not be considered true cells unless they had the characteristics of living things, including
  **a.** intelligence.
  **b.** nuclei.
  **c.** coacervates.
  **d.** heredity.

**In the space provided, write the letter of the description that best matches each term or phrase.**

_____ 5. radioactive isotopes

_____ 6. ribozyme

_____ 7. microspheres

_____ 8. RNA

_____ 9. radioactive decay

_____ 10. endosymbiosis

**a.** a measurable process that enables scientists to estimate the age of rocks and some fossils

**b.** RNA molecule that can act as a catalyst

**c.** the theory that mitochondria and chloroplasts evolved from symbiotic aerobic prokaryotes

**d.** thought to have been the forerunners of the first cells

**e.** thought to have catalyzed the assembly of the first proteins

**f.** unstable isotopes that break down and give off energy or particles

Assessment

# History of Life

In the space provided, write the letter of the term or phrase that best completes each statement or best answers each question.

_____ 1. What principle states that living things come from other living things?
a. biogenesis                         c. endosymbiosis
b. spontaneous generation             d. chemosynthesis

_____ 2. Which mixture of gases is thought to have made up Earth's early atmosphere?
a. nitrogen, hydrogen, water vapor, ammonia, methane
b. carbon dioxide, nitrogen, oxygen, argon, ozone
c. ozone, water vapor, carbon dioxide, ammonia
d. methane, oxygen, hydrogen, argon, water vapor

_____ 3. Most scientists agree that the basic molecules of life could have formed spontaneously through simple chemistry on the early Earth. Which of the following was made by Miller and Urey in the laboratory?
a. ozone                    c. amino acids
b. DNA                      d. None of the above

_____ 4. Microspheres could not be considered true cells unless they had the characteristics of living things, including
a. intelligence.            c. coacervates.
b. nuclei.                  d. heredity.

In the space provided, write the letter of the description that best matches each term or phrase.

_____ 5. radioactive isotopes

_____ 6. ribozyme

_____ 7. microspheres

_____ 8. RNA

_____ 9. radioactive decay

_____ 10. endosymbiosis

a. a measurable process that enables scientists to estimate the age of rocks and some fossils

b. RNA molecule that can act as a catalyst

c. the theory that mitochondria and chloroplasts evolved from symbiotic aerobic prokaryotes

d. thought to have been the forerunners of the first cells

e. thought to have catalyzed the assembly of the first proteins

f. unstable isotopes that break down and give off energy or particles

Name _____ Class _____ Date _____

# Theory of Evolution

**In the space provided, write the letter of the term or phrase that best completes each statement or best answers each question.**

_____ 1. The fossil record
  **a.** will never be complete.
  **b.** provides evidence of evolution.
  **c.** is a record of Earth's past life-forms.
  **d.** All of the above

_____ 2. Darwin believed that Malthus's hypotheses about populations applied
  **a.** to all species.
  **c.** to all species except humans.
  **b.** to only the human population.
  **d.** to only a specific population.

_____ 3. A vestigial structure is one that is
  **a.** similar to a structure in another species.
  **b.** reduced in size and mostly useless.
  **c.** an embryological structure.
  **d.** a characteristic of vertebrates.

_____ 4. Darwin and Lamarck agreed that changes in species are linked to
  **a.** genetics.
  **b.** environmental conditions.
  **c.** use or disuse of physical features.
  **d.** acquired characteristics.

_____ 5. The process by which different species evolve similar characteristics is called
  **a.** coevolution.               **c.** convergent evolution.
  **b.** divergent evolution.        **d.** artificial selection.

**In the space provided, write the letter of the description that best matches the name of the scientist.**

_____ 6. Charles Darwin

_____ 7. Charles Lyell

_____ 8. Jean Baptiste Lamarck

_____ 9. Georges Cuvier

_____ 10. Nicolaus Steno

  **a.** theory of evolution by means of acquired characteristics

  **b.** *On the Origin of Species by Means of Natural Selection*

  **c.** principle of uniformitarianism

  **d.** principle of superposition

  **e.** idea of catastrophism

Assessment

# Theory of Evolution

In the space provided, write the letter of the term or phrase that best completes each statement or best answers each question.

_____ 1. The fossil record
   a. will never be complete.
   b. provides evidence of evolution.
   c. is a record of Earth's past life-forms.
   d. All of the above

_____ 2. Darwin believed that Malthus's hypotheses about populations applied
   a. to all species.
   b. to only the human population.
   c. to all species except humans.
   d. to only a specific population.

_____ 3. A vestigial structure is one that is
   a. similar to a structure in another species.
   b. reduced in size and mostly useless.
   c. an embryological structure.
   d. a characteristic of vertebrates.

_____ 4. Darwin and Lamarck agreed that changes in species are linked to
   a. genetics.
   b. environmental conditions.
   c. use or disuse of physical features.
   d. acquired characteristics.

_____ 5. The process by which different species evolve similar characteristics is called
   a. coevolution.
   b. divergent evolution.
   c. convergent evolution.
   d. artificial selection.

In the space provided, write the letter of the description that best matches the name of the scientist.

_____ 6. Charles Darwin

_____ 7. Charles Lyell

_____ 8. Jean Baptiste Lamarck

_____ 9. Georges Cuvier

_____ 10. Nicolaus Steno

a. theory of evolution by means of acquired characteristics

b. On the Origin of Species by Means of Natural Selection

c. principle of uniformitarianism

d. principle of superposition

e. idea of catastrophism

Assessment

# Population Genetics and Speciation

**In the space provided, write the letter of the term or phrase that best completes each statement or best answers each question.**

_____ **1.** The Hardy-Weinberg principle states that
     **a.** dominant alleles will replace recessive alleles over time.
     **b.** dominant alleles are more common than recessive alleles.
     **c.** genotype frequencies do not spontaneously change.
     **d.** evolutionary forces have no effect on allele frequencies.

_____ **2.** Which of the following is NOT an evolutionary force?
     **a.** mutations in DNA
     **b.** Hardy-Weinberg principle
     **c.** genetic drift in a small population
     **d.** natural selection

_____ **3.** The range of phenotypes shifts toward one extreme in
     **a.** stabilizing selection.      **c.** directional selection.
     **b.** disruptive selection.      **d.** natural selection.

**In the space provided, write the letter of the description that best matches the term or phrase.**

_____ **4.** gene flow

_____ **5.** mutation

_____ **6.** nonrandom mating

_____ **7.** genetic drift

_____ **8.** natural selection

**a.** A bird prefers to breed with a male that is a strong nest builder.

**b.** Ten members leave a population and three others join.

**c.** A change in DNA results in the absence of an amino acid.

**d.** Over time, the allele for sickle cell anemia is decreasing in the United States because it provides no advantage.

**e.** A small group of ferrets, some with rare pink noses, is separated from the main population, and they begin to reproduce more pink-nosed ferrets.

Assessment

# Population Genetics and Speciation

In the space provided, write the letter of the term or phrase that best completes each statement or best answers each question.

_____ 1. The Hardy-Weinberg principle states that
    a. dominant alleles will replace recessive alleles over time.
    b. dominant alleles are more common than recessive alleles.
    c. genotype frequencies do not spontaneously change.
    d. evolutionary forces have no effect on allele frequencies.

_____ 2. Which of the following is NOT an evolutionary force?
    a. mutations in DNA
    b. Hardy-Weinberg principle
    c. genetic drift in a small population
    d. natural selection

_____ 3. The range of phenotypes shifts toward one extreme in
    a. stabilizing selection.    c. directional selection.
    b. disruptive selection.    d. natural selection.

In the space provided, write the letter of the description that best matches the term or phrase.

_____ 4. gene flow

_____ 5. mutation

_____ 6. nonrandom mating

_____ 7. genetic drift

_____ 8. natural selection

a. A bird prefers to breed with a male that is a strong nest builder.

b. Ten members leave a population and three others join.

c. A change in DNA results in the absence of an amino acid.

d. Over time, the allele for sickle cell anemia is decreasing in the United States because it provides no advantage.

e. A small group of ferrets, some with rare pink noses, is separated from the main population, and they begin to reproduce more pink-nosed ferrets.

Name _____ Class _____ Date _____

# Classification of Organisms

**In the space provided, write the letter of the term or phrase that best completes each statement or best answers each question.**

_____ 1. The naturalist who developed the two-word naming system for organisms was
    **a.** Aristotle.              **c.** Willi Hennig.
    **b.** Carolus Linnaeus.     **d.** Terry Erwin.

_____ 2. Cladograms determine evolutionary relationships between organisms by examining
    **a.** the strength of a character.
    **b.** the degree of difference between organisms.
    **c.** shared ancestral characters.
    **d.** shared derived characters.

_____ 3. The characteristics that scientists use in cladistics are
    **a.** analogous structures.        **c.** convergent structures.
    **b.** shared derived characters.   **d.** shared homologous traits.

_____ 4. Which of the following lists the eight classification levels in proper descending order?
    **a.** domain, kingdom, phylum, class, order, family, genus, species
    **b.** kingdom, domain, phylum, order, class, family, genus, species
    **c.** kingdom, phylum, family, class, domain, order, genus, species
    **d.** phylum, kingdom, domain, class, order, family, genus, species

_____ 5. The basic biological unit of the Linnaean system is
    **a.** species.              **c.** phylum.
    **b.** genus.               **d.** kingdom.

**In the space provided, write the letter of the description that best matches the term or phrase.**

_____ 6. domain              **a.** contains genera

_____ 7. phylum              **b.** contains families

_____ 8. order                **c.** contains kingdoms

_____ 9. genus               **d.** contains classes

_____10. family              **e.** contains species

Assessment

# Classification of Organisms

**In the space provided, write the letter of the term or phrase that best completes each statement or best answers each question.**

_____ 1. The naturalist who developed the two-word naming system for organisms was
    a. Aristotle.
    b. Carolus Linnaeus.
    c. Willi Hennig.
    d. Terry Erwin.

_____ 2. Cladograms determine evolutionary relationships between organisms by examining
    a. the strength of a character.
    b. the degree of difference between organisms.
    c. shared ancestral characters.
    d. shared derived characters.

_____ 3. The characteristics that scientists use in cladistics are
    a. analogous structures.
    b. shared derived characters.
    c. convergent structures.
    d. shared homologous traits.

_____ 4. Which of the following lists the eight classification levels in proper descending order?
    a. domain, kingdom, phylum, class, order, family, genus, species
    b. kingdom, domain, phylum, order, class, family, genus, species
    c. kingdom, phylum, family, class, domain, order, genus, species
    d. phylum, kingdom, domain, class, order, family, genus, species

_____ 5. The basic biological unit of the Linnaean system is
    a. species.
    b. genus.
    c. phylum.
    d. kingdom.

**In the space provided, write the letter of the description that best matches the term or phrase.**

_____ 6. domain      a. contains genera

_____ 7. phylum      b. contains families

_____ 8. order      c. contains kingdoms

_____ 9. genus      d. contains classes

_____ 10. family      e. contains species

Name _____ Class _____ Date _____

# Introduction to Ecology

**In the space provided, write the letter of the term or phrase that best completes each statement or best answers each question.**

_____ 1. A habitat is different from an ecosystem in that
   **a.** a habitat contains many ecosystems.
   **b.** an ecosystem can contain many habitats.
   **c.** a habitat is called a community.
   **d.** an ecosystem is the physical aspects of a habitat.

_____ 2. Most of life on Earth depends on which of the following?
   **a.** animals that eat plants
   **b.** photosynthetic organisms
   **c.** animals that eat other animals
   **d.** consumers on the second trophic level

_____ 3. Which process brings carbon into the living portion of its cycle?
   **a.** photosynthesis
   **b.** cellular respiration
   **c.** combustion
   **d.** decomposition

_____ 4. The lowest trophic level of any ecosystem is occupied by organisms such as
   **a.** lions, wolves, and snakes.
   **b.** humans, bears, and pigs.
   **c.** cows, horses, and caterpillars.
   **d.** plants, bacteria, and algae.

_____ 5. All of the following are biogeochemical cycles EXCEPT
   **a.** water.
   **b.** carbon.
   **c.** energy.
   **d.** phosphorus.

**In the space provided, write the letter of the description that best matches the term or phrase.**

_____ 6. biotic factor

_____ 7. abiotic factor

_____ 8. carnivore

_____ 9. transpiration

_____ 10. ecosystem

   **a.** a nonliving or physical aspect of a habitat
   **b.** evaporation of water through plant leaves
   **c.** a community and all its physical aspects
   **d.** a living or biological aspect of a habitat
   **e.** organism that eats other consumers

# Introduction to Ecology

In the space provided, write the letter of the term or phrase that best completes each statement or best answers each question.

_____ 1. A habitat is different from an ecosystem in that
   a. a habitat contains many ecosystems.
   b. an ecosystem can contain many habitats.
   c. a habitat is called a community.
   d. an ecosystem is the physical aspects of a habitat.

_____ 2. Most of life on Earth depends on which of the following?
   a. animals that eat plants
   b. photosynthetic organisms
   c. animals that eat other animals
   d. consumers on the second trophic level

_____ 3. Which process brings carbon into the living portion of its cycle?
   a. photosynthesis
   b. cellular respiration
   c. combustion
   d. decomposition

_____ 4. The lowest trophic level of any ecosystem is occupied by organisms such as
   a. lions, wolves, and snakes.          c. cows, horses, and caterpillars.
   b. humans, bears, and pigs.           d. plants, bacteria, and algae.

_____ 5. All of the following are biogeochemical cycles EXCEPT
   a. water.          c. energy.
   b. carbon.         d. phosphorus.

In the space provided, write the letter of the description that best matches the term or phrase.

_____ 6. biotic factor        a. a nonliving or physical aspect of a habitat

_____ 7. abiotic factor       b. evaporation of water through plant leaves

_____ 8. carnivore            c. a community and all its physical aspects

_____ 9. transpiration        d. a living or biological aspect of a habitat

_____ 10. ecosystem           e. organism that eats other consumers

Assessment

# Populations

**In the space provided, write the letter of the term or phrase that best completes each statement or best answers each question.**

_____ 1. The three main patterns of dispersion in a population are
  **a.** nonrandomly spaced, uniformly spaced, and clumped distribution.
  **b.** nonrandomly spaced, uniformly spaced, and unevenly spaced.
  **c.** randomly spaced, uniformly spaced, and clumped distribution.
  **d.** randomly spaced, uniformly spaced, and unevenly spaced.

_____ 2. A school of fish in the ocean, when seen from a distance, displays which type of dispersion?
  **a.** clumped                    **c.** random
  **b.** uniform                    **d.** None of the above

_____ 3. Which of the following is a density-dependent factor that may limit population growth?
  **a.** climate change             **c.** habitat destruction
  **b.** forest fire                **d.** spread of disease

_____ 4. In the exponential model of population growth, the growth rate
  **a.** remains constant.          **c.** increases.
  **b.** keeps changing.            **d.** increases and then decreases.

_____ 5. In a logistical model, exponential growth is limited by
  **a.** a density-independent factor.   **c.** the carrying capacity.
  **b.** an unknown factor.              **d.** an exponential factor.

_____ 6. What major change occurred 10,000 to 12,000 years ago that allowed the human population to rapidly increase?
  **a.** the industrial revolution
  **b.** the agricultural revolution
  **c.** a transition to a hunter-gatherer lifestyle
  **d.** a major outbreak of the bubonic plague

_____ 7. Which type of survivorship curve do most insects have?
  **a.** Type I                     **c.** Type III
  **b.** Type II                    **d.** None of the above

_____ 8. The four processes that directly determine a population's growth rate are birth, death, immigration, and
  **a.** carrying capacity.         **c.** dispersion.
  **b.** life expectancy.           **d.** emigration.

Assessment

# Populations

In the space provided, write the letter of the term or phrase that best completes each statement or best answers each question.

_____ 1. The three main patterns of dispersion in a population are
    a. nonrandomly spaced, uniformly spaced, and clumped distribution.
    b. nonrandomly spaced, uniformly spaced, and unevenly spaced.
    c. randomly spaced, uniformly spaced, and clumped distribution.
    d. randomly spaced, uniformly spaced, and unevenly spaced.

_____ 2. A school of fish in the ocean, when seen from a distance, displays which type of dispersion?
    a. clumped           c. random
    b. uniform          d. None of the above

_____ 3. Which of the following is a density-dependent factor that may limit population growth?
    a. climate change      c. habitat destruction
    b. forest fire         d. spread of disease

_____ 4. In the exponential model of population growth, the growth rate
    a. remains constant.      c. increases.
    b. keeps changing.       d. increases and then decreases.

_____ 5. In a logistical model, exponential growth is limited by
    a. a density-independent factor.    c. the carrying capacity.
    b. an unknown factor.        d. an exponential factor.

_____ 6. What major change occurred 10,000 to 12,000 years ago that allowed the human population to rapidly increase?
    a. the industrial revolution
    b. the agricultural revolution
    c. a transition to a hunter-gatherer lifestyle
    d. a major outbreak of the bubonic plague

_____ 7. Which type of survivorship curve do most insects have?
    a. Type I          c. Type III
    b. Type II         d. None of the above

_____ 8. The four processes that directly determine a population's growth rate are birth, death, immigration, and
    a. carrying capacity.     c. dispersion.
    b. life expectancy.      d. emigration.

**Assessment**

# Community Ecology

**In the space provided, write the letter of the term or phrase that best completes each statement or best answers each question.**

_____ 1. When two species compete for limited resources, competitive exclusion
   **a.** is sure to take place.
   **b.** is not possible.
   **c.** will take place unless the two species separate or find different resources.
   **d.** will cause both species to become extinct.

_____ 2. In parasitism, the host
   **a.** is killed by the parasite.        **c.** is benefited by the parasite.
   **b.** usually kills the parasite.        **d.** often transmits the parasite's offspring to new hosts.

_____ 3. *Chthamalus stellatus* can live high up out of water and low down in water within the intertidal zone. This is the barnacle's
   **a.** fundamental niche.        **c.** community.
   **b.** realized niche.        **d.** habitat.

_____ 4. Which pair of organisms exists in a commensal relationship?
   **a.** bear and fish        **c.** cattle egret and Cape buffalo
   **b.** ant and *Acacia* plant        **d.** dog and flea

_____ 5. What is the principle that enables five species of warbler to feed in the same tree without competing?
   **a.** commensalism        **c.** mutualism
   **b.** resource partitioning        **d.** competitive exclusion

**In the space provided, write the letter of the description that best matches the term or phrase.**

_____ 6. primary succession

_____ 7. predation

_____ 8. parasitism

_____ 9. mutualism

_____10. species evenness

**a.** relative abundance of each species in a community

**b.** one organism feeds on and usually lives on or in another larger organism

**c.** development of community in an area such as a bare rock

**d.** one organism killing and eating another for food

**e.** a symbiotic relationship in which both members benefit

Assessment

# Community Ecology

In the space provided, write the letter of the term or phrase that best completes each statement or best answers each question.

_____ 1. When two species compete for limited resources, competitive exclusion
a. is sure to take place.
b. is not possible.
c. will take place unless the two species separate or find different resources.
d. will cause both species to become extinct.

_____ 2. In parasitism, the host
a. is killed by the parasite.
b. usually kills the parasite.
c. is benefited by the parasite.
d. often transmits the parasite's offspring to new hosts.

_____ 3. Chthamalus stellatus can live high up out of water and low down in water within the intertidal zone. This is the barnacle's
a. fundamental niche.
b. realized niche.
c. community.
d. habitat.

_____ 4. Which pair of organisms exists in a commensal relationship?
a. bear and fish
b. ant and Acacia plant
c. cattle egret and Cape buffalo
d. dog and flea

_____ 5. What is the principle that enables five species of warbler to feed in the same tree without competing?
a. commensalism
b. resource partitioning
c. mutualism
d. competitive exclusion

In the space provided, write the letter of the description that best matches the term or phrase.

_____ 6. primary succession

_____ 7. predation

_____ 8. parasitism

_____ 9. mutualism

_____ 10. species evenness

a. relative abundance of each species in a community

b. one organism feeds on and usually lives on or in another larger organism

c. development of community in an area such as a bare rock

d. one organism killing and eating another for food

e. a symbiotic relationship in which both members benefit

Assessment

# Ecosystems

**In the space provided, write the letter of the term or phrase that best completes each statement or best answers each question.**

_____ 1. What is the most productive terrestrial biome?
   **a.** estuaries
   **b.** taiga
   **c.** tropical forests
   **d.** temperate deciduous forests

_____ 2. What type of vegetation dominates in the taiga biome?
   **a.** deciduous trees
   **b.** coniferous trees
   **c.** mosses, lichens, and dwarf woody plants
   **d.** tall grasses and scattered trees

_____ 3. The open ocean beyond the continental shelf is classified as the
   **a.** neritic zone.          **c.** aphotic zone.
   **b.** benthic zone.          **d.** pelagic zone.

_____ 4. A freshwater aquatic ecosystem that contains high amounts of organic matter and vegetation, with murky water is known as a(n)
   **a.** oligotrophic lake.
   **b.** river.
   **c.** estuary.
   **d.** eutrophic lake.

_____ 5. Cacti and plants with a waxy coating on their leaves are typical vegetation in a(n)
   **a.** desert.
   **b.** chaparral.
   **c.** savanna.
   **d.** taiga.

**In the space provided, write the letter of the description that best matches the term or phrase.**

_____ 6. photic zone          **a.** orchids and bromeliads

_____ 7. epiphyte          **b.** the ocean bottom

_____ 8. benthic zone          **c.** organisms that drift with ocean currents

_____ 9. canopy          **d.** part of ocean that receives sunlight

_____ 10. plankton          **e.** continuous treetop layer

Name _____ Class _____ Date _____

Assessment

# Ecosystems

In the space provided, write the letter of the term or phrase that best completes each statement or best answers each question.

_____ 1. What is the most productive terrestrial biome?
   a. estuaries
   b. taiga
   c. tropical forests
   d. temperate deciduous forests

_____ 2. What type of vegetation dominates in the taiga biome?
   a. deciduous trees
   b. coniferous trees
   c. mosses, lichens, and dwarf woody plants
   d. tall grasses and scattered trees

_____ 3. The open ocean beyond the continental shelf is classified as the
   a. neritic zone.        c. aphotic zone.
   b. benthic zone.        d. pelagic zone.

_____ 4. A freshwater aquatic ecosystem that contains high amounts of organic matter and vegetation, with murky water is known as a(n)
   a. oligotrophic lake.
   b. river.
   c. estuary.
   d. eutrophic lake.

_____ 5. Cacti and plants with a waxy coating on their leaves are typical vegetation in a(n)
   a. desert.
   b. chaparral.
   c. savanna.
   d. taiga.

In the space provided, write the letter of the description that best matches the term or phrase.

_____ 6. photic zone          a. orchids and bromeliads
_____ 7. epiphyte             b. the ocean bottom
_____ 8. benthic zone         c. organisms that drift with ocean currents
_____ 9. canopy               d. part of ocean that receives sunlight
_____ 10. plankton            e. continuous treetop layer

Copyright © by Holt, Rinehart and Winston. All rights reserved.

Modern Biology          41          Quiz

# Humans and the Environment

**In the space provided, write the letter of the description that best matches the term or phrase.**

_____ **1.** acid precipitation

_____ **2.** global warming

_____ **3.** CFCs

_____ **4.** ultraviolet radiation

_____ **5.** ozone

_____ **6.** greenhouse effect

**a.** class of chemicals used as coolants that can break down and destroy ozone

**b.** the absorption of solar energy by insulating gases such as carbon dioxide

**c.** creates a protective shield in the upper atmosphere

**d.** a period of more than a century with steadily increasing average temperatures worldwide

**e.** exposure to this can damage DNA and cause mutations which can lead to cancer

**f.** precipitation with a low pH

**In the space provided, write the letter of the term or phrase that best completes each statement or best answers each question.**

_____ **7.** A pesticide that is now banned, but previously caused problems with predatory bird eggs during reproduction is
   **a.** chlordane.
   **b.** lindane.
   **c.** DDT.
   **d.** dieldrin.

_____ **8.** People paying local guides to show them a unique ecosystem and its organisms is an example of
   **a.** a debt-for-nature swap.
   **b.** ecotourism.
   **c.** a biodiversity hotspot.
   **d.** conservation biology.

_____ **9.** Greenhouse gases include
   **a.** carbon dioxide.
   **b.** methane.
   **c.** CFCs.
   **d.** Both a and b

_____ **10.** A species that has a critical function in an ecosystem is known as a(n)
   **a.** keystone species.
   **b.** bioindicator.
   **c.** extinct species.
   **d.** hotspot species.

Assessment

# Humans and the Environment

In the space provided, write the letter of the description that best matches the term or phrase.

_____ 1. acid precipitation

_____ 2. global warming

_____ 3. CFCs

_____ 4. ultraviolet radiation

_____ 5. ozone

_____ 6. greenhouse effect

a. class of chemicals used as coolants that can break down and destroy ozone

b. the absorption of solar energy by insulating gases such as carbon dioxide

c. creates a protective shield in the upper atmosphere

d. a period of more than a century with steadily increasing average temperatures worldwide

e. exposure to this can damage DNA and cause mutations which can lead to cancer

f. precipitation with a low pH

In the space provided, write the letter of the term or phrase that best completes each statement or best answers each question.

_____ 7. A pesticide that is now banned, but previously caused problems with predatory bird eggs during reproduction is
　　a. chlordane.
　　b. lindane.
　　c. DDT.
　　d. dieldrin.

_____ 8. People paying local guides to show them a unique ecosystem and its organisms is an example of
　　a. a debt-for-nature swap.
　　b. ecotourism.
　　c. a biodiversity hotspot.
　　d. conservation biology.

_____ 9. Greenhouse gases include
　　a. carbon dioxide.
　　b. methane.
　　c. CFCs.
　　d. Both a and b

_____ 10. A species that has a critical function in an ecosystem is known as a(n)
　　a. keystone species.
　　b. bioindicator.
　　c. extinct species.
　　d. hotspot species.

# Bacteria

**In the space provided, write the letter of the description that best matches the term or phrase.**

_____ **1.** toxins

_____ **2.** coccus

_____ **3.** pili

_____ **4.** bacillus

_____ **5.** antibiotics

_____ **6.** spirillum

**a.** short outgrowths that enable bacteria to attach to surfaces or to other cells

**b.** chemicals secreted by bacteria that are poisonous to eukaryotic cells

**c.** chemicals that interfere with life processes in bacteria

**d.** a rod-shaped bacterium

**e.** a round-shaped bacterium

**f.** a spiral-shaped bacterium

**In the space provided, write the letter of the term or phrase that best completes each statement or best answers each question.**

_____ **7.** Bacterial chromosomes consist of which of the following?
   **a.** a single circular piece of DNA
   **b.** linear pieces of DNA
   **c.** DNA in paired chromosomes
   **d.** DNA or RNA in various forms

_____ **8.** All of the following are groups of bacteria EXCEPT
   **a.** Archaea.
   **b.** Proteobacteria.
   **c.** Cyanobacteria.
   **d.** Chlamydia.

_____ **9.** Farmers rotate their crops regularly and grow legumes in order to
   **a.** destroy harmful bacteria in the soil.
   **b.** grow crops with antibiotic properties.
   **c.** create an aerobic environment in the soil.
   **d.** utilize bacteria to increase nitrogen in the soil.

_____ **10.** A type of bacterium that commonly causes food poisoning is
   **a.** *Streptococcus mutans.*
   **b.** *Escherichia coli.*
   **c.** *Clostridium tetani.*
   **d.** *Bacillus thuringiensis.*

Assessment

# Bacteria

In the space provided, write the letter of the description that best matches the term or phrase.

_____ 1. toxins

_____ 2. coccus

_____ 3. pili

_____ 4. bacillus

_____ 5. antibiotics

_____ 6. spirillum

a. short outgrowths that enable bacteria to attach to surfaces or to other cells

b. chemicals secreted by bacteria that are poisonous to eukaryotic cells

c. chemicals that interfere with life processes in bacteria

d. a rod-shaped bacterium

e. a round-shaped bacterium

f. a spiral-shaped bacterium

In the space provided, write the letter of the term or phrase that best completes each statement or best answers each question.

_____ 7. Bacterial chromosomes consist of which of the following?
   a. a single circular piece of DNA
   b. linear pieces of DNA
   c. DNA in paired chromosomes
   d. DNA or RNA in various forms

_____ 8. All of the following are groups of bacteria EXCEPT
   a. Archaea.
   b. Proteobacteria.
   c. Cyanobacteria.
   d. Chlamydia.

_____ 9. Farmers rotate their crops regularly and grow legumes in order to
   a. destroy harmful bacteria in the soil.
   b. grow crops with antibiotic properties.
   c. create an aerobic environment in the soil.
   d. utilize bacteria to increase nitrogen in the soil.

_____ 10. A type of bacterium that commonly causes food poisoning is
   a. *Streptococcus mutans*.
   b. *Escherichia coli*.
   c. *Clostridium tetani*.
   d. *Bacillus thuringiensis*.

Name _____ Class _____ Date _____

# Viruses

**In the space provided, write the letter of the description that best matches the term or phrase.**

_____ **1.** capsid

_____ **2.** lytic cycle

_____ **3.** prion

_____ **4.** provirus

_____ **5.** bacteriophage

_____ **6.** viroid

**a.** a viral gene that is inserted into a host chromosome

**b.** a virus that infects bacteria

**c.** the protein coat of a virus

**d.** how virulent viruses replicate

**e.** infectious single strand of RNA with no capsid

**f.** infectious protein with no nucleic acid

**In the space provided, write the letter of the term or phrase that best completes each statement or best answers each question.**

_____ **7.** The nucleic acid of a virus consists of which of the following?
  **a.** DNA
  **b.** RNA
  **c.** both DNA and RNA
  **d.** either DNA or RNA

_____ **8.** Most scientists think that early viruses originated from
  **a.** other viruses.
  **b.** existing cell parts.
  **c.** animals.
  **d.** spontaneous generation.

_____ **9.** HIV causes AIDS by
  **a.** converting a proto-oncogene to an oncogene.
  **b.** damaging a person's blood vessels.
  **c.** destroying the covering of a person's nerves.
  **d.** gradually destroying a person's immune system.

_____ **10.** Which of the following is NOT a vector of viral diseases?
  **a.** mosquitoes
  **b.** ticks
  **c.** bacteria
  **d.** humans

Name _____ Class _____ Date _____

Assessment

# Viruses

In the space provided, write the letter of the description that best matches the term or phrase.

_____ 1. capsid

_____ 2. lytic cycle

_____ 3. prion

_____ 4. provirus

_____ 5. bacteriophage

_____ 6. viroid

a. a viral gene that is inserted into a host chromosome

b. a virus that infects bacteria

c. the protein coat of a virus

d. how virulent viruses replicate

e. infectious single strand of RNA with no capsid

f. infectious protein with no nucleic acid

In the space provided, write the letter of the term or phrase that best completes each statement or best answers each question.

_____ 7. The nucleic acid of a virus consists of which of the following?
a. DNA
b. RNA
c. both DNA and RNA
d. either DNA or RNA

_____ 8. Most scientists think that early viruses originated from
a. other viruses.
b. existing cell parts.
c. animals.
d. spontaneous generation.

_____ 9. HIV causes AIDS by
a. converting a proto-oncogene to an oncogene.
b. damaging a person's blood vessels.
c. destroying the covering of a person's nerves.
d. gradually destroying a person's immune system.

_____ 10. Which of the following is NOT a vector of viral diseases?
a. mosquitoes
b. ticks
c. bacteria
d. humans

Name _____ Class _____ Date _____

Assessment

# Protists

**In the space provided, write the letter of the description that best matches the term or phrase.**

_____ **1.** thallus

_____ **2.** red algae

_____ **3.** dinoflagellates

_____ **4.** sporozoite

_____ **5.** euglenoids

_____ **6.** plasmodial slime molds

_____ **7.** oomycotes

**a.** freshwater protists with two flagella; reproduce by mitosis; some are photosynthetic; some are heterotrophic

**b.** unicellular phototrophs; most have two flagella; most are marine and make up part of plankton; cause red tides

**c.** water molds that produce fertilization tubes

**d.** protists that can live at great ocean depths

**e.** plantlike body portion of a seaweed

**f.** produce stalked fruiting bodies when food is scarce

**g.** Part of a *Plasmodium* life cycle

**In the space provided, write the letter of the term or phrase that best completes each statement or best answers each question.**

_____ **8.** Amoebas move using extensions of cytoplasm called
   **a.** cilia.
   **b.** flagella.
   **c.** pseudopodia.
   **d.** tests.

_____ **9.** Because the euglenoid's pellicle is flexible, this organism can
   **a.** move toward the light.
   **b.** survive in a dark environment.
   **c.** reproduce sexually.
   **d.** change shape.

_____ **10.** *Paramecium* takes in food through its
   **a.** contractile vacuoles.
   **b.** cilia-lined oral groove.
   **c.** flexible outer pellicle.
   **d.** two nuclei.

Assessment

# Protists

In the space provided, write the letter of the description that best matches the term or phrase.

_____ 1. thallus

_____ 2. red algae

_____ 3. dinoflagellates

_____ 4. sporozoite

_____ 5. euglenoids

_____ 6. plasmodial slime molds

_____ 7. oomycotes

a. freshwater protists with two flagella; reproduce by mitosis; some are photosynthetic; some are heterotrophic

b. unicellular phototropics; most have two flagella; most are marine and make up part of plankton; cause red tides

c. water molds that produce fertilization tubes

d. protists that can live at great ocean depths

e. plantlike body portion of a seaweed

f. produce stalked fruiting bodies when food is scarce

g. Part of a *Plasmodium* life cycle

In the space provided, write the letter of the term or phrase that best completes each statement or best answers each question.

_____ 8. Amoebas move using extensions of cytoplasm called

a. cilia.

b. flagella.

c. pseudopodia.

d. tests.

_____ 9. Because the euglenoid's pellicle is flexible, this organism can

a. move toward the light.

b. survive in a dark environment.

c. reproduce sexually.

d. change shape.

_____ 10. *Paramecium* takes in food through its

a. contractile vacuoles.

b. cilia-lined oral groove.

c. flexible outer pellicle.

d. two nuclei.

Name _____ Class _____ Date _____

# Fungi

**In the space provided, write the letter of the description that best matches the term or phrase. Some choices may be used more than once.**

_____ 1. grows on bread

_____ 2. causes athlete's foot

_____ 3. source of certain antibiotics

_____ 4. breaks down fallen leaves and tree stumps

_____ 5. causes ringworm

_____ 6. baker's yeast

_____ 7. produces flavor and aroma of certain cheeses

**a.** parasite that absorbs nutrients from living host

**b.** resource recycler

**c.** commercially valuable

**In the space provided, write the letter of the term or phrase that best completes each statement or best answers each question.**

_____ 8. A typical fungus
   **a.** contains chlorophyll.
   **b.** is immobile.
   **c.** has cell walls made of chitin.
   **d.** Both (b) and (c)

_____ 9. Fungi obtain nutrients by
   **a.** taking in food particles and digesting them internally.
   **b.** capturing microorganisms that live in the soil.
   **c.** breaking down organic material in their environment and digesting it.
   **d.** using sunlight to make carbohydrates.

_____ 10. Fungi reproduce asexually by releasing which of the following?
   **a.** lightweight spores
   **b.** thick-walled resistant zygotes
   **c.** very small seeds
   **d.** fast-swimming sperm

Assessment

# Fungi

In the space provided, write the letter of the description that best matches the term or phrase. Some choices may be used more than once.

_____ 1. grows on bread

_____ 2. causes athlete's foot

_____ 3. source of certain antibiotics

_____ 4. breaks down fallen leaves and tree stumps

_____ 5. causes ringworm

_____ 6. baker's yeast

_____ 7. produces flavor and aroma of certain cheeses

a. parasite that absorbs nutrients from living host

b. resource recycler

c. commercially valuable

In the space provided, write the letter of the term or phrase that best completes each statement or best answers each question.

_____ 8. A typical fungus
a. contains chlorophyll.
b. is immobile.
c. has cell walls made of chitin.
d. Both (b) and (c)

_____ 9. Fungi obtain nutrients by
a. taking in food particles and digesting them internally.
b. capturing microorganisms that live in the soil.
c. breaking down organic material in their environment and digesting it.
d. using sunlight to make carbohydrates.

_____ 10. Fungi reproduce asexually by releasing which of the following?
a. lightweight spores
b. thick-walled resistant zygotes
c. very small seeds
d. fast-swimming sperm

Name _____ Class _____ Date _____

Assessment

# The Importance of Plants

**In the space provided, write the letter of the term or phrase that best completes each statement or best answers each question.**

_____ 1. Which of the following is an example of a root crop?
    **a.** wheat                 **c.** an artichoke
    **b.** a mango             **d.** a potato

_____ 2. The study of plants is called
    **a.** botany.                **c.** agriculture.
    **b.** biology.               **d.** plant ecology.

_____ 3. Plant varieties that have been grown and selected by people and have at least one distinguishing characteristic are called
    **a.** cereals.                **c.** crops.
    **b.** cultivars.            **d.** fruits.

_____ 4. What is the most important interaction between plants and the environment?
    **a.** recycling of iron from the soil
    **b.** production of pollen that causes hay fever
    **c.** the capture of solar energy through photosynthesis
    **d.** crowding out of crop plants by weeds

_____ 5. Which of the following plants would be LEAST likely to cause the allergic reaction of hay fever?
    **a.** wild grasses         **c.** oak trees
    **b.** ragweed            **d.** roses

**Complete each statement by writing the correct term or phrase in the space provided.**

6. The growing of plants and the raising of animals for human use is called

_____ .

7. _____ are members of the pea family and bear seeds in pods.

8. To improve crop yields, _____ are used to supply plants with essential mineral nutrients.

9. Many plants species form mycorrhizae, which are symbiotic relationships between _____ and plant roots.

10. The pollen that commonly causes the allergic reaction of hay fever comes from small, drab flowers that are pollinated by the _____ .

Assessment

# The Importance of Plants

In the space provided, write the letter of the term or phrase that best completes each statement or best answers each question.

_____ 1. Which of the following is an example of a root crop?
   a. wheat
   b. a mango
   c. an artichoke
   d. a potato

_____ 2. The study of plants is called
   a. botany.
   b. biology.
   c. agriculture.
   d. plant ecology.

_____ 3. Plant varieties that have been grown and selected by people and have at least one distinguishing characteristic are called
   a. cereals.
   b. cultivars.
   c. crops.
   d. fruits.

_____ 4. What is the most important interaction between plants and the environment?
   a. recycling of iron from the soil
   b. production of pollen that causes hay fever
   c. the capture of solar energy through photosynthesis
   d. crowding out of crop plants by weeds

_____ 5. Which of the following plants would be LEAST likely to cause the allergic reaction of hay fever?
   a. wild grasses
   b. ragweed
   c. oak trees
   d. roses

Complete each statement by writing the correct term or phrase in the space provided.

6. The growing of plants and the raising of animals for human use is called

   _____

7. _____ are members of the pea family and bear seeds in pods

8. To improve crop yields, _____ are used to supply plants with essential mineral nutrients.

9. Many plants species form mycorrhizae, which are symbiotic relationships between _____ and plant roots.

10. The pollen that commonly causes the allergic reaction of hay fever comes from small, drab flowers that are pollinated by the _____ .

Assessment

# Plant Evolution and Classification

**In the space provided, write the letter of the description that best matches the term or phrase.**

_____ 1. spores

_____ 2. alternation of generations

_____ 3. bryophytes

_____ 4. seed

_____ 5. cotyledons

**a.** cycle including a gametophyte and a sporophyte

**b.** three phyla of nonvascular plants

**c.** haploid reproductive cell with hard outer wall

**d.** contains a plant embryo

**e.** seed leaves

**In the space provided, write the letter of the term or phrase that best completes each statement or best answers each question.**

_____ 6. Which of the following characteristics is NOT a survival advantage for life on land?
  **a.** vascular tissue
  **b.** seeds
  **c.** pollen
  **d.** swimming sperm

_____ 7. Xylem and phloem function like
  **a.** tubes.
  **b.** windows.
  **c.** plastic wrap.
  **d.** anchors.

_____ 8. Unlike mosses, ferns have
  **a.** seeds.
  **b.** vascular tissue.
  **c.** a dominant gametophyte generation.
  **d.** tiny fruits.

_____ 9. In gymnosperms, male and female gametophytes develop within
  **a.** cones.
  **b.** flowers.
  **c.** seeds.
  **d.** fruits.

_____ 10. Bryophytes need water
  **a.** to reproduce asexually.
  **b.** to form sperm cells.
  **c.** to reproduce sexually.
  **d.** to support their long stems.

Assessment

# Plant Evolution and Classification

In the space provided, write the letter of the description that best matches the term or phrase.

_____ 1. spores

_____ 2. alternation of generations

_____ 3. bryophytes

_____ 4. seed

_____ 5. cotyledons

a. cycle including a gametophyte and a sporophyte
b. three phyla of nonvascular plants
c. haploid reproductive cell with hard outer wall
d. contains a plant embryo
e. seed leaves

In the space provided, write the letter of the term or phrase that best completes each statement or best answers each question.

_____ 6. Which of the following characteristics is NOT a survival advantage for life on land?
a. vascular tissue
b. seeds
c. pollen
d. swimming sperm

_____ 7. Xylem and phloem function like
a. tubes.
b. windows.
c. plastic wrap.
d. anchors.

_____ 8. Unlike mosses, ferns have
a. seeds.
b. vascular tissue.
c. a dominant gametophyte generation.
d. tiny fruits.

_____ 9. In gymnosperms, male and female gametophytes develop within
a. cones.
b. flowers.
c. seeds.
d. fruits.

_____ 10. Bryophytes need water
a. to reproduce asexually.
b. to form sperm cells.
c. to reproduce sexually.
d. to support their long stems.

# Plant Structure and Function

**In the space provided, write the letter of the description that best matches the term or phrase.**

_____ **1.** transpiration

_____ **2.** vessel element

_____ **3.** root cap

_____ **4.** translocation

**a.** the movement of organic compounds within a plant

**b.** mass of cells that covers an actively growing root tip

**c.** the loss of water vapor by a plant

**d.** type of xylem cell with large holes in its ends

**In the space provided, write the letter of the term or phrase that best completes each statement or best answers each question.**

_____ **5.** Dermal tissue functions in
   **a.** protection.
   **b.** gas exchange.
   **c.** absorption of mineral nutrients.
   **d.** All of the above

_____ **6.** In plants, organic compounds move from a source to a
   **a.** root.
   **b.** stoma.
   **c.** sink.
   **d.** guard cell.

_____ **7.** In plants, guard cells control the rate of
   **a.** water loss.
   **b.** root growth.
   **c.** sugar movement.
   **d.** leaf formation.

_____ **8.** Much of the inside of the nonwoody parts of a plant is
   **a.** dermal tissue.
   **b.** ground tissue.
   **c.** epidermis.
   **d.** vascular tissue.

_____ **9.** Which of the following can be considered an example of a sink?
   **a.** leaf
   **b.** developing apple
   **c.** woody twig
   **d.** potato

_____ **10.** Sugars move through
   **a.** sieve-tube cells.
   **b.** companion cells.
   **c.** vessels.
   **d.** tracheids.

Assessment

# Plant Structure and Function

In the space provided, write the letter of the description that best matches the term or phrase.

_____ 1. transpiration

_____ 2. vessel element

_____ 3. root cap

_____ 4. translocation

a. the movement of organic compounds within a plant

b. mass of cells that covers an actively growing root tip

c. the loss of water vapor by a plant

d. type of xylem cell with large holes in its ends

In the space provided, write the letter of the term or phrase that best completes each statement or best answers each question.

_____ 5. Dermal tissue functions in
   a. protection.
   b. gas exchange
   c. absorption of mineral nutrients.
   d. All of the above

_____ 6. In plants, organic compounds move from a source to a
   a. root.          c. sink.
   b. stoma.         d. guard cell.

_____ 7. In plants, guard cells control the rate of
   a. water loss.     c. sugar movement.
   b. root growth.    d. leaf formation.

_____ 8. Much of the inside of the nonwoody parts of a plant is
   a. dermal tissue.   c. epidermis.
   b. ground tissue.   d. vascular tissue.

_____ 9. Which of the following can be considered an example of a sink?
   a. leaf
   b. developing apple
   c. woody twig
   d. potato

_____ 10. Sugars move through
   a. sieve-tube cells.
   b. companion cells.
   c. vessels.
   d. tracheids.

Assessment

# Plant Reproduction

**In the space provided, write the letter of the description that best matches the term or phrase.**

_____ 1. sepal

_____ 2. cutting

_____ 3. anther

_____ 4. sorus

_____ 5. sporophyte

**a.** protects a flower while it is still a bud

**b.** contains sporangia in ferns

**c.** location of male gametophytes in angiosperms

**d.** a piece of a leaf, stem, or root

**e.** the spore-producing generation of a seedless plant

**In the space provided, write the letter of the term or phrase that best completes each statement or best answers each question.**

_____ 6. Compared to their sporophytes, the gametophytes of seed plants are
   **a.** much smaller.
   **b.** the same size.
   **c.** much larger.
   **d.** variable in size throughout the life cycle.

_____ 7. A pollen grain contains
   **a.** endosperm.                **c.** sperm.
   **b.** an embryo.                 **d.** Both (b) and (c)

_____ 8. Which of the following is NOT an example of vegetative propagation?
   **a.** seeds
   **b.** runners
   **c.** rhizomes
   **d.** tubers

_____ 9. When a moss spore settles to the ground, it germinates and produces
   **a.** a "leafy" green gametophyte.
   **b.** a stalklike sporophyte.
   **c.** sperm.
   **d.** a small, green, heart-shaped gametophyte.

_____ 10. The male parts of the flower are called
   **a.** sepals.
   **b.** pistils.
   **c.** stamens.
   **d.** ovaries.

Assessment

# Plant Reproduction

**In the space provided, write the letter of the description that best matches the term or phrase.**

_____ 1. sepal

_____ 2. cutting

_____ 3. anther

_____ 4. sorus

_____ 5. sporophyte

a. protects a flower while it is still a bud
b. contains sporangia in ferns
c. location of male gametophytes in angiosperms
d. a piece of a leaf, stem, or root
e. the spore-producing generation of a seedless plant

**In the space provided, write the letter of the term or phrase that best completes each statement or best answers each question.**

_____ 6. Compared to their sporophytes, the gametophytes of seed plants are
   a. much smaller.
   b. the same size.
   c. much larger.
   d. variable in size throughout the life cycle.

_____ 7. A pollen grain contains
   a. endosperm.
   b. an embryo.
   c. sperm.
   d. Both (b) and (c)

_____ 8. Which of the following is NOT an example of vegetative propagation?
   a. seeds
   b. runners
   c. rhizomes
   d. tubers

_____ 9. When a moss spore settles to the ground, it germinates and produces
   a. a "leafy" green gametophyte.
   b. a stalklike sporophyte.
   c. sperm.
   d. a small, green, heart-shaped gametophyte.

_____ 10. The male parts of the flower are called
   a. sepals.
   b. pistils.
   c. stamens.
   d. ovaries.

# Plant Responses

**In the space provided, write the letter of the description that best matches the term or phrase.**

_____ **1.** dormancy

_____ **2.** hormones

_____ **3.** tropism

_____ **4.** auxin

_____ **5.** photoperiodism

_____ **6.** apical dominance

**a.** response in which a plant grows either toward or away from a stimulus

**b.** growth-promoting chemical that causes stems to bend

**c.** condition in which a plant or a seed remains inactive

**d.** plant's response to changes in length of days and nights

**e.** chemicals produced in one part of an organism and transported to another part, where it causes a response

**f.** inhibition of growth of buds along a stem

**In the space provided, write the letter of the term or phrase that best completes each statement or best answers each question.**

_____ **7.** Experiment with auxin uncovered the chemical cause of
    **a.** phototropism.
    **b.** gravitropism.
    **c.** thigmotropism.
    **d.** photoperiodism.

_____ **8.** A hormone that is produced in root tips and stimulates cell division and promotes lateral bud growth in flowers is
    **a.** auxin.
    **b.** gibberellin.
    **c.** cytokinin.
    **d.** agar.

_____ **9.** Applying naphthaline acid to the cut tips of the stems of a plant causes
    **a.** fruit to drop off.
    **b.** the plant to die.
    **c.** lateral buds to grow.
    **d.** lateral buds to be dormant.

_____ **10.** Plants whose growth and development are NOT affected by day length are known as
    **a.** short-day plants.
    **b.** long-day plants.
    **c.** day-neutral plants.
    **d.** None of the above

# Plant Responses

**In the space provided, write the letter of the description that best matches the term or phrase.**

_____ **1.** dormancy

_____ **2.** hormones

_____ **3.** tropism

_____ **4.** auxin

_____ **5.** photoperiodism

_____ **6.** apical dominance

a. response in which a plant grows either toward or away from a stimulus

b. growth-promoting chemical that causes stems to bend

c. condition in which a plant or a seed remains inactive

d. plant's response to changes in length of days and nights

e. chemicals produced in one part of an organism and transported to another part, where it causes a response

f. inhibition of growth of buds along a stem

**In the space provided, write the letter of the term or phrase that best completes each statement or best answers each question.**

_____ **7.** Experiment with auxin uncovered the chemical cause of
  a. phototropism.
  b. gravitropism.
  c. thigmotropism.
  d. photoperiodism.

_____ **8.** A hormone that is produced in root tips and stimulates cell division and promotes lateral bud growth in flowers is
  a. auxin.
  b. gibberellin.
  c. cytokinin.
  d. agar.

_____ **9.** Applying naphthaline acid to the cut tips of the stems of a plant causes
  a. fruit to drop off.
  b. the plant to die.
  c. lateral buds to grow.
  d. lateral buds to be dormant.

_____ **10.** Plants whose growth and development are NOT affected by day length are known as
  a. short-day plants.
  b. long-day plants.
  c. day-neutral plants.
  d. None of the above

Assessment

# Introduction to Animals

**In the space provided, write the letter of the term or phrase that best completes each statement or best answers each question.**

_____ **1.** All animals
    **a.** are heterotrophs.
    **b.** have ectoderm, endoderm, and mesoderm.
    **c.** reproduce asexually.
    **d.** are bilaterally symmetrical.

_____ **2.** Sponges digest their food
    **a.** in the coelom.
    **b.** in a gastrovascular cavity.
    **c.** extracellularly.
    **d.** intracellularly.

_____ **3.** The difference between a closed circulatory system and an open circulatory system is that
    **a.** an open system does not have vessels, but a closed system has.
    **b.** a closed system does not have vessels, but an open system has.
    **c.** blood does not leave the vessels in a closed system.
    **d.** blood does not leave the vessels in an open system.

_____ **4.** A coelom
    **a.** occurs in radially symmetrical animals.
    **b.** is located within the endoderm.
    **c.** protects internal organs from the movement of surrounding muscles.
    **d.** exists in all animals.

**In the space provided, write the letter of the description that best matches the term or phrase.**

_____ **5.** radial symmetry

_____ **6.** blastula

_____ **7.** exoskeleton

_____ **8.** acoelomate

_____ **9.** asymmetry

_____ **10.** comparing embryos

**a.** the type of symmetry found in sponges

**b.** protects internal organs

**c.** a way to determine animal relationships

**d.** the type of symmetry found in jellyfish

**e.** having no body cavity

**f.** a hollow ball of cells

Assessment

# Introduction to Animals

In the space provided, write the letter of the term or phrase that best completes each statement or best answers each question.

_____ 1. All animals
    a. are heterotrophs.            c. reproduce asexually.
    b. have ectoderm, endoderm,    d. are bilaterally symmetrical.
       and mesoderm.

_____ 2. Sponges digest their food
    a. in the coelom.             c. extracellularly.
    b. in a gastrovascular cavity.   d. intracellularly.

_____ 3. The difference between a closed circulatory system and an open circulatory system is that
    a. an open system does not have vessels, but a closed system has.
    b. a closed system does not have vessels, but an open system has.
    c. blood does not leave the vessels in a closed system.
    d. blood does not leave the vessels in an open system.

_____ 4. A coelom
    a. occurs in radially symmetrical animals.
    b. is located within the endoderm.
    c. protects internal organs from the movement of surrounding muscles.
    d. exists in all animals.

In the space provided, write the letter of the description that best matches the term or phrase.

_____ 5. radial symmetry           a. the type of symmetry found in sponges

_____ 6. blastula               b. protects internal organs

                            c. a way to determine animal relationships

_____ 7. exoskeleton           d. the type of symmetry found in jellyfish

_____ 8. acoelomate           e. having no body cavity

_____ 9. asymmetry            f. a hollow ball of cells

_____ 10. comparing embryos

Assessment

# Sponges, Cnidarians, and Ctenophores

**In the space provided, write the letter of the description that best matches the term or phrase.**

_____ **1.** ostia

_____ **2.** oscula

_____ **3.** choanocyte

_____ **4.** cnidocytes

_____ **5.** planula

_____ **6.** comb jelly

**a.** water, along with wastes, exits

**b.** lines the internal cavity of a sponge

**c.** lacks cnidocytes

**d.** nutrient-rich water enters

**e.** unique to cnidarians

**f.** develops into a polyp

**In the space provided, write the letter of the term or phrase that best completes each statement or best answers each question.**

_____ **7.** Evidence of cell recognition in sponges is shown by the
   **a.** presence of choanocytes.
   **b.** sessile behavior of sponges.
   **c.** ability of sponge cells to recombine and form a new sponge.
   **d.** presence of tissues and organs.

_____ **8.** Choanocytes are involved in which of the following?
   **a.** sponge reproduction
   **b.** sponge feeding
   **c.** waste removal
   **d.** All of the above

_____ **9.** Which class of cnidarians has no medusa stage?
   **a.** Anthozoa
   **b.** Hydrozoa
   **c.** Scyphozoa
   **d.** None of the above

_____ **10.** Hydras and anemones are both
   **a.** hydrozoans.
   **b.** anthozoans.
   **c.** parasitic.
   **d.** sessile.

Assessment

# Sponges, Cnidarians, and Ctenophores

**In the space provided, write the letter of the description that best matches the term or phrase.**

_____ 1. ostia

_____ 2. osculum

_____ 3. choanocyte

_____ 4. cnidocytes

_____ 5. planula

_____ 6. comb jelly

a. water, along with wastes, exits

b. lines the internal cavity of a sponge

c. lacks cnidocytes

d. nutrient-rich water enters

e. unique to cnidarians

f. develops into a polyp

**In the space provided, write the letter of the term or phrase that best completes each statement or best answers each question.**

_____ 7. Evidence of cell recognition in sponges is shown by the
   a. presence of choanocytes.
   b. sessile behavior of sponges.
   c. ability of sponge cells to recombine and form a new sponge.
   d. presence of tissues and organs.

_____ 8. Choanocytes are involved in which of the following?
   a. sponge reproduction
   b. sponge feeding
   c. waste removal
   d. All of the above

_____ 9. Which class of cnidarians has no medusa stage?
   a. Anthozoa
   b. Hydrozoa
   c. Scyphozoa
   d. None of the above

_____ 10. Hydras and anemones are both
   a. hydrozoans.
   b. anthozoans.
   c. parasitic.
   d. sessile.

# Flatworms, Roundworms, and Rotifers

**In the space provided, write the letter of the description that best matches the term or phrase.**

_____ **1.** endoparasite

_____ **2.** ectoparasite

_____ **3.** proglottid

_____ **4.** pseudocoelom

_____ **5.** planarians

_____ **6.** cestodes and trematodes

**a.** parasitic flatworms

**b.** a complete reproductive unit

**c.** lives on the external surface of the host

**d.** free-living flatworms

**e.** lives inside the host

**f.** evolutionary milestone in roundworms

**In the space provided, write the letter of the term or phrase that best completes each statement or best answers each question.**

_____ **7.** *Ascaris* is
   **a.** an ectoparasite.
   **b.** free-living.
   **c.** an endoparasite.
   **d.** a trematode.

_____ **8.** Rotifers grind food with which of the following?
   **a.** cloaca
   **b.** mouth
   **c.** mastax
   **d.** intestine

_____ **9.** A person may become infected with endoparasites by any of the following EXCEPT
   **a.** ingesting their eggs.
   **b.** standing in water contaminated with their larvae.
   **c.** ingesting their larvae.
   **d.** not washing daily.

_____ **10.** Tapeworms absorb food from the host's intestine through which of the following?
   **a.** tegument
   **b.** mouth
   **c.** digestive system
   **d.** collar cells

Name _____ Class _____ Date _____

Assessment

# Flatworms, Roundworms, and Rotifers

In the space provided, write the letter of the description that best matches the term or phrase.

_____ 1. endoparasite

_____ 2. ectoparasite

_____ 3. proglottid

_____ 4. pseudocoelom

_____ 5. planarians

_____ 6. cestodes and trematodes

a. parasitic flatworms
b. a complete reproductive unit
c. lives on the external surface of the host
d. free-living flatworms
e. lives inside the host
f. evolutionary milestone in roundworms

In the space provided, write the letter of the term or phrase that best completes each statement or best answers each question.

_____ 7. Ascaris is
a. an ectoparasite.
b. free-living.
c. an endoparasite.
d. a trematode.

_____ 8. Rotifers grind food with which of the following?
a. cloaca
b. mouth
c. mastax
d. intestine

_____ 9. A person may become infected with endoparasites by any of the following EXCEPT
a. ingesting their eggs.
b. standing in water contaminated with their larvae.
c. ingesting their larvae.
d. not washing daily

_____ 10. Tapeworms absorb food from the host's intestine through which of the following?
a. tegument
b. mouth
c. digestive system
d. collar cells

Name _____  Class _____  Date _____

# Mollusks and Annelids

**In the space provided, write the letter of the term or phrase that best completes each statement or best answers each question.**

_____ 1. One characteristic that is shared by all mollusks and annelids is a(n)
   **a.** segmented body.
   **b.** open circulatory system.
   **c.** coelom.
   **d.** distinctive head region.

_____ 2. Bivalves are unlike other mollusks because bivalves do NOT have a
   **a.** shell.            **c.** radula.
   **b.** mantle.           **d.** foot.

_____ 3. An earthworm ingests soil by using a muscular structure called a
   **a.** pharynx.          **c.** crop.
   **b.** esophagus.        **d.** gizzard.

_____ 4. Which of the following structures are found in leeches?
   **a.** suckers           **c.** parapodia
   **b.** setae             **d.** All of the above

**In the space provided, write the letter of the description that best matches the term or phrase.**

_____ 5. parapodia

_____ 6. trochophore

_____ 7. radula

_____ 8. setae

_____ 9. crop

_____ 10. adductor muscles

**a.** a larval stage that is present in mollusks and annelids

**b.** bristles on the external surface of most annelids

**c.** appendages used for swimming, crawling, and gas exchange

**d.** structures that, when contracted, cause the hinged shell of a bivalve to close

**e.** storage chamber in an earthworm's digestive tract

**f.** structure used by some mollusks to scrape fragments of food off rocks

Assessment

# Mollusks and Annelids

In the space provided, write the letter of the term or phrase that best completes each statement or best answers each question.

_____ 1. One characteristic that is shared by all mollusks and annelids is a(n)
  a. segmented body.
  b. open circulatory system.
  c. coelom.
  d. distinctive head region.

_____ 2. Bivalves are unlike other mollusks because they do NOT have a
  a. shell.          c. radula.
  b. mantle.          d. foot.

_____ 3. An earthworm ingests soil by using a muscular structure called a
  a. pharynx.          c. crop.
  b. esophagus.          d. gizzard.

_____ 4. Which of the following structures are found in leeches?
  a. suckers          c. parapodia
  b. setae          d. All of the above

In the space provided, write the letter of the description that best matches the term or phrase.

_____ 5. parapodia

_____ 6. trochophore

_____ 7. radula

_____ 8. setae

_____ 9. crop

_____ 10. adductor muscles

a. a larval stage that is present in mollusks and annelids

b. bristles on the external surface of most annelids

c. appendages used for swimming, crawling, and gas exchange

d. structures that, when contracted, cause the hinged shell of a bivalve to close

e. storage chamber in an earthworm's digestive tract

f. structure used by some mollusks to scrape fragments of food off rocks

Assessment

# Arthropods

**In the space provided, write the letter of the description that best matches the term or phrase.**

_____ **1.** Chelicerata

_____ **2.** Crustacea

_____ **3.** cephalothorax

_____ **4.** abdomen

_____ **5.** uropods

_____ **6.** swimmerets

**a.** body section to which the legs of an arachnid are attached

**b.** appendages attached to the underside of a lobster's abdomen

**c.** body section that contains most of a spider's organs

**d.** subphylum that includes arthropods with fangs or pincers

**e.** flattened, paddlelike structures at the end of a lobster's abdomen

**f.** subphylum that includes shrimps and pill bugs

**In the space provided, write the letter of the term or phrase that best completes each statement or best answers each question.**

_____ **7.** Which of the following is a characteristic of all arthropods?
   **a.** jaws
   **b.** simple, single-lens eyes
   **c.** parapodia
   **d.** jointed appendages

_____ **8.** Which of the following is NOT a characteristic of most scorpions?
   **a.** tropical habitat
   **b.** an unsegmented body
   **c.** a venomous stinger
   **d.** large, grasping pincers

_____ **9.** Which structures do crustaceans use for respiration?
   **a.** gills
   **b.** book lungs
   **c.** tracheae
   **d.** spiracles

_____ **10.** The head, thorax, and abdomen of mites
   **a.** are separate segmented sections.
   **b.** form two sections, the cephalothorax and the abdomen.
   **c.** are fused to form a single body.
   **d.** form two sections, the head and a fused thorax and abdomen.

Assessment

# Arthropods

**In the space provided, write the letter of the description that best matches the term or phrase.**

_____ 1. Chelicerata

_____ 2. Crustacea

_____ 3. cephalothorax

_____ 4. abdomen

_____ 5. uropods

_____ 6. swimmerets

a. body section to which the legs of an arachnid are attached

b. appendages attached to the underside of a lobster's abdomen

c. body section that contains most of a spider's organs

d. subphylum that includes arthropods with fangs or pincers

e. flattened, paddlelike structures at the end of a lobster's abdomen

f. subphylum that includes shrimps and pill bugs

**In the space provided, write the letter of the term or phrase that best completes each statement or best answers each question.**

_____ 7. Which of the following is a characteristic of all arthropods?
a. jaws
b. simple, single-lens eyes
c. parapodia
d. jointed appendages

_____ 8. Which of the following is NOT a characteristic of most scorpions?
a. tropical habitat
b. an unsegmented body
c. a venomous stinger
d. large, grasping pincers

_____ 9. Which structures do crustaceans use for respiration?
a. gills
b. book lungs
c. tracheae
d. spiracles

_____ 10. The head, thorax, and abdomen of mites
a. are separate segmented sections.
b. form two sections, the cephalothorax and the abdomen.
c. are fused to form a single body.
d. form two sections, the head and a fused thorax and abdomen.

Name _____ Class _____ Date _____

Assessment

# Insects

**In the space provided, write the letter of the description that best matches the term or phrase.**

_____ 1. ovipositor

_____ 2. chrysalis

_____ 3. social insect

_____ 4. maxilla

_____ 5. pheromone

_____ 6. pupa

**a.** helps honeybees recognize the hive

**b.** an insect mouthpart

**c.** a structure used by a female grasshopper to dig a hole before she lays eggs

**d.** a stage in the life cycle of some insects

**e.** lives in a hive

**f.** a protective capsule that encloses some insects during part of their life cycle

**In the space provided, write the letter of the term or phrase that best completes each statement or best answers each question.**

_____ 7. Which of the following characteristics is NOT shared by all insects?
  **a.** three body sections
  **b.** one pair of wings
  **c.** three pairs of legs
  **d.** one pair of antennae

_____ 8. As a young insect molts, it undergoes a process of physical change called
  **a.** segmentation.
  **b.** reproduction.
  **c.** metamorphosis.
  **d.** evolution.

_____ 9. An insect's wings are attached to its
  **a.** head.
  **b.** appendages.
  **c.** abdomen.
  **d.** thorax.

_____ 10. The thorax of a grasshopper has three pairs of
  **a.** eyes.
  **b.** legs.
  **c.** antennae.
  **d.** mouthparts.

Copyright © by Holt, Rinehart and Winston. All rights reserved.
Modern Biology 73 Quiz

# Insects

**In the space provided, write the letter of the description that best matches the term or phrase.**

_____ **1.** ovipositor

_____ **2.** chrysalis

_____ **3.** social insect

_____ **4.** maxilla

_____ **5.** pheromone

_____ **6.** pupa

a. helps honeybees recognize the hive
b. an insect mouthpart
c. a structure used by a female grasshopper to dig a hole before she lays eggs
d. a stage in the life cycle of some insects
e. lives in a hive
f. a protective capsule that encloses some insects during part of their life cycle

**In the space provided, write the letter of the term or phrase that best completes each statement or best answers each question.**

_____ **7.** Which of the following characteristics is NOT shared by all insects?
a. three body sections          c. three pairs of legs
b. one pair of wings           d. one pair of antennae

_____ **8.** As a young insect molts, it undergoes a process of physical change called
a. segmentation.
b. reproduction.
c. metamorphosis.
d. evolution.

_____ **9.** An insect's wings are attached to its
a. head.
b. appendages.
c. abdomen.
d. thorax.

_____ **10.** The thorax of a grasshopper has three pairs of
a. eyes.
b. legs.
c. antennae.
d. mouthparts.

Name _____ Class _____ Date _____

Assessment

# Echinoderms and Invertebrate Chordates

**In the space provided, write the letter of the description that best matches the term or phrase.**

_____ 1. madreporite

_____ 2. tunicate

_____ 3. incurrent siphon

_____ 4. postanal tail

_____ 5. sea cucumber

_____ 6. sea urchin

a. a chordate that lacks a nerve cord as an adult

b. an armless echinoderm with protruding spines

c. an armless echinoderm with a soft, sluglike body

d. the structure through which water enters a tunicate's body

e. a structure that extends beyond the anus

f. the structure through which water enters and leaves the water-vascular system

**In the space provided, write the letter of the term or phrase that best completes each statement or best answers each question.**

_____ 7. Most adult echinoderms have which of the following?
   a. an asymmetrical body
   b. five-part radial symmetry
   c. five-part bilateral symmetry
   d. two-part bilateral symmetry

_____ 8. Sea lilies and feather stars differ from all other living echinoderms because their mouth
   a. develops from the blastopore.
   b. is disk-shaped.
   c. is located on the lower surface.
   d. is located on the upper surface.

_____ 9. Which of the following is a sessile chordate?
   a. sea star
   b. tunicate
   c. lancelet
   d. sand dollar

_____ 10. Animals that have a notochord but do NOT have a backbone are called
   a. protostomes.
   b. echinoderms.
   c. vertebrates.
   d. invertebrate chordates.

Assessment

# Echinoderms and Invertebrate Chordates

In the space provided, write the letter of the description that best matches the term or phrase.

_____ 1. madreporite

_____ 2. tunicate

_____ 3. incurrent siphon

_____ 4. postanal tail

_____ 5. sea cucumber

_____ 6. sea urchin

a. a chordate that lacks a nerve cord as an adult

b. an armless echinoderm with protruding spines

c. an armless echinoderm with a soft, sluglike body

d. the structure through which water enters a tunicate's body

e. a structure that extends beyond the anus

f. the structure through which water enters and leaves the water-vascular system

In the space provided, write the letter of the term or phrase that best completes each statement or best answers each question.

_____ 7. Most adult echinoderms have which of the following?
a. an asymmetrical body
b. five-part radial symmetry
c. five-part bilateral symmetry
d. two-part bilateral symmetry

_____ 8. Sea lilies and feather stars differ from all other living echinoderms because their mouth
a. develops from the blastopore.
b. is disk-shaped.
c. is located on the lower surface.
d. is located on the upper surface.

_____ 9. Which of the following is a sessile chordate?
a. sea star
b. tunicate
c. lancelet
d. sand dollar

_____ 10. Animals that have a notochord but do NOT have a backbone are called
a. protostomes.
b. echinoderms.
c. vertebrates.
d. invertebrate chordates.

Assessment

# Fishes

**In the space provided, write the letter of the description that best matches the term or phrase.**

_____ **1.** gill filament

_____ **2.** sinus venosus

_____ **3.** conus arteriosus

_____ **4.** skate

_____ **5.** lamprey

**a.** area of heart that smooths pulsations of the blood

**b.** cartilaginous fish with a flattened body

**c.** parasitic fish with a structure like a suction cup around its mouth

**d.** collection area of a fish's heart

**e.** structure through which gases enter and leave a fish's blood

**In the space provided, write the letter of the term or phrase that best completes each statement or best answers each question.**

_____ **6.** Fish "swallow" water to
   **a.** force it from the mouth and over the gills.
   **b.** steady themselves in the water.
   **c.** feed.
   **d.** All of the above

_____ **7.** In most fishes, blood circulates from the heart to the
   **a.** rest of the body, to the gills, and back to the heart.
   **b.** gills, to the rest of the body, and back to the heart.
   **c.** gills, back to the heart, and to the rest of the body.
   **d.** lungs, to the rest of the body, and back to the heart.

_____ **8.** To rise in the water, a bony fish fills its swim bladder with gas from
   **a.** its gills.
   **b.** its bloodstream.
   **c.** the surrounding water.
   **d.** its lungs.

_____ **9.** Jawless fishes have which of the following?
   **a.** unpaired fins
   **b.** scales
   **c.** bony skeletons
   **d.** swim bladders

_____ **10.** The yellow perch is an example of a
   **a.** lobe-finned fish.
   **b.** jawless fish.
   **c.** cartilaginous fish.
   **d.** ray-finned fish.

# Fishes

**In the space provided, write the letter of the description that best matches the term or phrase.**

_____ 1. gill filament

_____ 2. sinus venosus

_____ 3. conus arteriosus

_____ 4. skate

_____ 5. lamprey

a. area of heart that smooths pulsations of the blood

b. cartilaginous fish with a flattened body

c. parasitic fish with a structure like a suction cup around its mouth

d. collection area of a fish's heart

e. structure through which gases enter and leave a fish's blood

**In the space provided, write the letter of the term or phrase that best completes each statement or best answers each question.**

_____ 6. Fish "swallow" water to
a. force it from the mouth and over the gills.
b. steady themselves in the water.
c. feed.
d. All of the above

_____ 7. In most fishes, blood circulates from the heart to the
a. rest of the body, to the gills, and back to the heart.
b. gills, to the rest of the body, and back to the heart.
c. gills, back to the heart, and to the rest of the body.
d. lungs, to the rest of the body, and back to the heart.

_____ 8. To rise in the water, a bony fish fills its swim bladder with gas from
a. its gills.
b. its bloodstream.
c. the surrounding water.
d. its lungs.

_____ 9. Jawless fishes have which of the following?
a. unpaired fins
b. scales
c. bony skeletons
d. swim bladders

_____ 10. The yellow perch is an example of a
a. lobe-finned fish.
b. jawless fish.
c. cartilaginous fish.
d. ray-finned fish.

# Amphibians

**In the space provided, write the letter of the description that best matches the term or phrase.**

_____ **1.** cutaneous respiration

_____ **2.** metamorphosis

_____ **3.** caecilian

_____ **4.** tadpole

_____ **5.** postive-pressure breathing

_____ **6.** salamander

**a.** pumping of air into the lungs

**b.** physical change from larva to adult

**c.** long-tailed amphibian with an elongated body

**d.** skin breathing

**e.** legless, burrowing amphibian

**f.** fishlike, larval form of a frog

**In the space provided, write the letter of the term or phrase that best completes each statement or best answers each question.**

_____ **7.** In a modern amphibian's heart,
   **a.** neither the atrium nor the ventricle is divided.
   **b.** both the atrium and the ventricle are divided.
   **c.** only the ventricle is divided.
   **d.** only the atrium is divided.

_____ **8.** Frogs and toads are members of which order?
   **a.** Anura
   **b.** Caudata
   **c.** Gymnophiona
   **d.** Cloaca

_____ **9.** The digestive system of adult amphibians is
   **a.** adapted mainly to a carnivorous diet.
   **b.** adapted mainly to a diet of water plants.
   **c.** not specialized for various functions.
   **d.** Both (a) and (b)

_____ **10.** A frog's pulmonary veins carry blood from the
   **a.** body organs.
   **b.** atria.
   **c.** lungs.
   **d.** ventricle.

Assessment

# Amphibians

In the space provided, write the letter of the description that best matches the term or phrase.

_____ 1. cutaneous respiration

_____ 2. metamorphosis

_____ 3. caecilian

_____ 4. tadpole

_____ 5. positive-pressure breathing

_____ 6. salamander

a. pumping of air into the lungs
b. physical change from larva to adult
c. long-tailed amphibian with an elongated body
d. skin breathing
e. legless, burrowing amphibian
f. fishlike, larval form of a frog

In the space provided, write the letter of the term or phrase that best completes each statement or best answers each question.

_____ 7. In a modern amphibian's heart,
a. neither the atrium nor the ventricle is divided.
b. both the atrium and the ventricle are divided.
c. only the ventricle is divided.
d. only the atrium is divided.

_____ 8. Frogs and toads are members of which order?
a. Anura
b. Caudata
c. Gymnophiona
d. Cloaca

_____ 9. The digestive system of adult amphibians is
a. adapted mainly to a carnivorous diet.
b. adapted mainly to a diet of water plants.
c. not specialized for various functions.
d. Both (a) and (b)

_____ 10. A frog's pulmonary veins carry blood from the
a. body organs.
b. atria.
c. lungs.
d. ventricle.

Assessment

# Reptiles

**In the space provided, write the letter of the description that best matches the term or phrase.**

_____ 1. caiman

_____ 2. tortoise

_____ 3. Jacobson's organ

_____ 4. python

_____ 5. thecodont

**a.** reptile in the order Crocodilia

**b.** reptile in the order Squamata

**c.** odor-sensing depression in a rattlesnake's mouth

**d.** extinct crocodile-like reptile

**e.** reptile with dome-shaped shell

**In the space provided, write the letter of the term or phrase that best completes each statement or best answers each question.**

_____ 6. Which of the following helps to explain the success of dinosaurs?
  **a.** ectothermy
  **b.** co-existence with birds, which were less competitive
  **c.** reduced competition for resources due to mass extinctions
  **d.** a favorably wet climate

_____ 7. Which structure does a timber rattlesnake use to locate warm-bodied animals in total darkness?
  **a.** venom gland     **b.** tongue     **c.** pits below the eyes     **d.** rattle

_____ 8. The problem of sperm and eggs drying out on land is solved in reptiles by which of the following?
  **a.** internal fertilization
  **b.** the amniotic egg
  **c.** overlapping scales
  **d.** Both (a) and (b)

_____ 9. Lizards decrease their body temperature by
  **a.** absorbing heat from their environment.
  **b.** increasing their rate of metabolism.
  **c.** staying in the shade.
  **d.** basking in the sun.

_____ 10. The skin of reptiles
  **a.** contains a protein called Keratin.
  **b.** loses a lot of water through evaporation.
  **c.** functions as a respiratory surface.
  **d.** All of the above

Assessment

# Reptiles

**In the space provided, write the letter of the description that best matches the term or phrase.**

_____ 1. caiman

_____ 2. tortoise

_____ 3. Jacobson's organ

_____ 4. python

_____ 5. thecodont

a. reptile in the order Crocodilia

b. reptile in the order Squamata

c. odor-sensing depression in a rattlesnake's mouth

d. extinct crocodile-like reptile

e. reptile with dome-shaped shell

**In the space provided, write the letter of the term or phrase that best completes each statement or best answers each question.**

_____ 6. Which of the following helps to explain the success of dinosaurs?
a. ectothermy
b. co-existence with birds, which were less competitive
c. reduced competition for resources due to mass extinctions
d. a favorably wet climate

_____ 7. Which structure does a timber rattlesnake use to locate warm-bodied animals in total darkness?
a. venom gland    b. tongue    c. pits below the eyes    d. rattle

_____ 8. The problem of sperm and eggs drying out on land is solved in reptiles by which of the following?
a. internal fertilization
b. the amniotic egg
c. overlapping scales
d. Both (a) and (b)

_____ 9. Lizards decrease their body temperature by
a. absorbing heat from their environment.
b. increasing their rate of metabolism.
c. staying in the shade.
d. basking in the sun.

_____ 10. The skin of reptiles
a. contains a protein called keratin.
b. loses a lot of water through evaporation.
c. functions as a respiratory surface.
d. All of the above

Name _____ Class _____ Date _____

Assessment

# Birds

**In the space provided, write the letter of the description that best matches the term or phrase.**

_____ **1.** duck

_____ **2.** raptor

_____ **3.** woodpecker

_____ **4.** heron

_____ **5.** songbird

_____ **6.** parrot

**a.** flattened beak

**b.** long legs for wading

**c.** short, stout, hooked beak

**d.** strong, chisel-like beak

**e.** toes that can cling to branches; one toe points backward

**f.** powerful, curved talons

**In the space provided, write the letter of the term or phrase that best completes each statement or best answers each question.**

_____ **7.** Birds satisfy their increased need for oxygen by having
  **a.** air sacs.
  **b.** one-way air flow through the lungs.
  **c.** a completely divided ventricle.
  **d.** All of the above

_____ **8.** The excretory system of birds
  **a.** is lightweight but inefficient.
  **b.** stores liquid wastes in a bladder.
  **c.** converts nitrogenous wastes to uric acid.
  **d.** absorbs nitrogenous wastes from the cloaca.

_____ **9.** The oldest known bird fossils are classified in the genus
  **a.** *Sinornis.*
  **b.** *Archaeopteryx.*
  **c.** *Ichthyornis.*
  **d.** *Hesperornis.*

_____ **10.** Which of the following is NOT an adaptation of birds for flight?
  **a.** webbed feet
  **b.** keeled breastbone
  **c.** thin, hollow bones
  **d.** fused collarbones

Assessment

# Birds

**In the space provided, write the letter of the description that best matches the term or phrase.**

_____ 1. duck

_____ 2. raptor

_____ 3. woodpecker

_____ 4. heron

_____ 5. songbird

_____ 6. parrot

a. flattened beak

b. long legs for wading

c. short, stout, hooked beak

d. strong, chisel-like beak

e. toes that can cling to branches; one toe points backward

f. powerful, curved talons

**In the space provided, write the letter of the term or phrase that best completes each statement or best answers each question.**

_____ 7. Birds satisfy their increased need for oxygen by having
  a. air sacs.
  b. one-way air flow through the lungs.
  c. a completely divided ventricle.
  d. All of the above

_____ 8. The excretory system of birds
  a. is lightweight but inefficient.
  b. stores liquid wastes in a bladder.
  c. converts nitrogenous wastes to uric acid.
  d. absorbs nitrogenous wastes from the cloaca.

_____ 9. The oldest known bird fossils are classified in the genus
  a. Sinornis.
  b. Archaeopteryx.
  c. Ichthyornis.
  d. Hesperornis.

_____ 10. Which of the following is NOT an adaptation of birds for flight?
  a. webbed feet
  b. keeled breastbone
  c. thin, hollow bones
  d. fused collarbones

# Mammals

**In the space provided, write the letter of the description that best matches the term or phrase.**

_____ **1.** therapsid

_____ **2.** monotreme

_____ **3.** primate

_____ **4.** hominid

_____ **5.** Order Chiroptera

_____ **6.** Order Proboscidea

**a.** a prosimian, a monkey, an ape, or a human

**b.** have elongated nose; largest land animals alive today

**c.** an egg-laying mammal

**d.** only mammals capable of true flight

**e.** ancestor of mammals

**f.** a primate that walks upright on two legs

**In the space provided, write the letter of the term or phrase that best completes each statement or best answers each question.**

_____ **7.** Australopithecines
   **a.** walked on all four limbs.
   **b.** walked upright on two legs.
   **c.** had brains as large as those of modern humans.
   **d.** had brains that were larger than those of modern humans.

_____ **8.** Which of the following is NOT a characteristic of mammals?
   **a.** hair
   **b.** specialized teeth
   **c.** ectothermic metabolism
   **d.** mammary glands

_____ **9.** Which type of tooth is commonly found in a carnivore and used for tearing flesh?
   **a.** incisor
   **b.** canine
   **c.** premolar
   **d.** molar

_____ **10.** The circulatory system of mammals features a
   **a.** two-chambered heart.
   **b.** three-chambered heart.
   **c.** four-chambered heart.
   **d.** multiple-heart system.

Assessment

# Mammals

In the space provided, write the letter of the description that best matches the term or phrase.

_____ 1. therapsid

_____ 2. monotreme

_____ 3. primate

_____ 4. hominid

_____ 5. Order Chiroptera

_____ 6. Order Proboscidea

a. a prosimian, a monkey, an ape, or a human
b. have elongated nose; largest land animals alive today
c. an egg-laying mammal
d. only mammals capable of true flight
e. ancestor of mammals
f. a primate that walks upright on two legs

In the space provided, write the letter of the term or phrase that best completes each statement or best answers each question.

_____ 7. Australopithecines
a. walked on all four limbs.
b. walked upright on two legs.
c. had brains as large as those of modern humans.
d. had brains that were larger than those of modern humans.

_____ 8. Which of the following is NOT a characteristic of mammals?
a. hair
b. specialized teeth
c. ectothermic metabolism
d. mammary glands

_____ 9. Which type of tooth is commonly found in a carnivore and used for tearing flesh?
a. incisor
b. canine
c. premolar
d. molar

_____ 10. The circulatory system of mammals features a
a. two-chambered heart.
b. three-chambered heart.
c. four-chambered heart.
d. multiple-heart system.

Assessment

# Animal Behavior

**In the space provided, write the letter of the description that best matches the term or phrase.**

_____ 1. territorial behavior

_____ 2. courtship behavior

_____ 3. parental care

_____ 4. migratory behavior

_____ 5. reasoning

_____ 6. innate behavior

_____ 7. imprinting

**a.** learning that forms permanent associations and occurs during a specific period early in the life of an animal

**b.** move to a more suitable environment as seasons change

**c.** ensure survival of young

**d.** protect a resource for exclusive use

**e.** inherited behavior, or instincts

**f.** attract a mate

**g.** the ability to solve a problem not previously encountered

**In the space provided, write the letter of the term or phrase that best completes each statement or best answers each question.**

_____ 8. Web building is a(n)
   **a.** innate behavior.
   **b.** learned behavior.
   **c.** result of reasoning.
   **d.** conditioned response.

_____ 9. Psychologist B.F. Skinner created a box that taught behavior to animals inside through
   **a.** classical conditioning.
   **b.** operant conditioning.
   **c.** fixed action pattern behavior.
   **d.** reasoning.

_____ 10. The choice of a mate based on a trait or set of traits is called
   **a.** sexual selection.
   **b.** competitive mating.
   **c.** reproductive characteristics.
   **d.** signaling.

Assessment

# Animal Behavior

In the space provided, write the letter of the description that best matches the term or phrase.

_____ 1. territorial behavior

_____ 2. courtship behavior

_____ 3. parental care

_____ 4. migratory behavior

_____ 5. reasoning

_____ 6. innate behavior

_____ 7. imprinting

a. learning that forms permanent associations and occurs during a specific period early in the life of an animal

b. move to a more suitable environment as seasons change

c. ensure survival of young

d. protect a resource for exclusive use

e. inherited behavior, or instincts

f. attract a mate

g. the ability to solve a problem not previously encountered

In the space provided, write the letter of the term or phrase that best completes each statement or best answers each question.

_____ 8. Web building is a(n)
a. innate behavior.
b. learned behavior.
c. result of reasoning.
d. conditioned response.

_____ 9. Psychologist B.F. Skinner created a box that taught behavior to animals inside through
a. classical conditioning.
b. operant conditioning.
c. fixed action pattern behavior.
d. reasoning.

_____ 10. The choice of a mate based on a trait or set of traits is called
a. sexual selection.
b. competitive mating.
c. reproductive characteristics.
d. signaling.

# Skeletal, Muscular, and Integumentary Systems

**In the space provided, write the letter of the description that best matches the term or phrase.**

_____ **1.** epithelial tissue

_____ **2.** osteocyte

_____ **3.** myofibril

_____ **4.** sarcomere

_____ **5.** epidermis

**a.** small, cylindrical structures within a muscle fiber

**b.** protects other tissues from dehydration and physical damage

**c.** outermost layer of skin

**d.** cell imbedded in bone tissue, which maintains the mineral content of bone

**e.** the area between two Z lines

**In the space provided, write the letter of the term or phrase that best completes each statement or best answers each question.**

_____ **6.** Which of the following organs is found in the cranial cavity?
  **a.** stomach               **c.** brain
  **b.** spinal cord           **d.** heart

_____ **7.** Red bone marrow produces
  **a.** fat.                  **c.** blood vessels.
  **b.** bone cells.           **d.** blood cells and platelets.

_____ **8.** A muscle contraction begins when
  **a.** a sarcomere is fully contracted.
  **b.** a muscle fiber is stimulated by a nerve cell.
  **c.** a myosin head detaches from an actin filament.
  **d.** ATP binds to actin.

_____ **9.** Which of the following structures are NOT found in the dermis?
  **a.** nerve cells           **c.** blood vessels
  **b.** hair follicles        **d.** cells that produce melanin

_____ **10.** Which of the following structures or substance is NOT found in epidermis?
  **a.** keratin               **c.** sweat gland
  **b.** hair                  **d.** pore

Assessment

# Skeletal, Muscular, and Integumentary Systems

**In the space provided, write the letter of the description that best matches the term or phrase.**

_____ 1. epithelial tissue

_____ 2. osteocyte

_____ 3. myofibril

_____ 4. sarcomere

_____ 5. epidermis

a. small, cylindrical structures within a muscle fiber

b. protects other tissues from dehydration and physical damage

c. outermost layer of skin

d. cell imbedded in bone tissue, which maintains the mineral content of bone

e. the area between two Z lines

**In the space provided, write the letter of the term or phrase that best completes each statement or best answers each question.**

_____ 6. Which of the following organs is found in the cranial cavity?
a. stomach
b. spinal cord
c. brain
d. heart

_____ 7. Red bone marrow produces
a. fat.
b. bone cells.
c. blood vessels.
d. blood cells and platelets.

_____ 8. A muscle contraction begins when
a. a sarcomere is fully contracted.
b. a muscle fiber is stimulated by a nerve cell.
c. a myosin head detaches from an actin filament.
d. ATP binds to actin.

_____ 9. Which of the following structures are NOT found in the dermis?
a. nerve cells
b. hair follicles
c. blood vessels
d. cells that produce melanin

_____ 10. Which of the following structures or substance is NOT found in epidermis?
a. keratin
b. hair
c. sweat gland
d. pore

Name _____ Class _____ Date _____

**Assessment**

# Circulatory and Respiratory Systems

**In the space provided, write the letter of the description that best matches the term or phrase.**

_____ 1. left ventricle

_____ 2. right atrium

_____ 3. left atrium

_____ 4. right ventricle

_____ 5. type O blood

_____ 6. type AB blood

**a.** chamber that receives deoxygenated blood from the body

**b.** chamber that pumps blood to the lungs

**c.** chamber that receives oxygenated blood from the lungs

**d.** chamber that pumps blood to the body

**e.** universal recipient

**f.** universal donor

**In the space provided, write the letter of the term or phrase that best completes each statement or best answers each question.**

_____ 7. Antigens on the surface of red blood cells include
   **a.** A antigens.
   **b.** B antigens.
   **c.** Rh antigens.
   **d.** All of the above

_____ 8. Which of the following vessel walls has a thickness of only one cell layer?
   **a.** artery
   **b.** capillary
   **c.** vein
   **d.** arteriole

_____ 9. What occurs when the air pressure in the lungs is higher than in the atmosphere?
   **a.** inhalation
   **b.** the diaphragm contracts
   **c.** exhalation
   **d.** the rib cage moves up and out

_____ 10. The site(s) of gas exchange in the lungs is
   **a.** the bronchi.
   **b.** the alveoli.
   **c.** the bronchioles.
   **d.** All of the above

Assessment

# Circulatory and Respiratory Systems

In the space provided, write the letter of the description that best matches the term or phrase.

_____ 1. left ventricle

_____ 2. right atrium

_____ 3. left atrium

_____ 4. right ventricle

_____ 5. type O blood

_____ 6. type AB blood

a. chamber that receives deoxygenated blood from the body

b. chamber that pumps blood to the lungs

c. chamber that receives oxygenated blood from the lungs

d. chamber that pumps blood to the body

e. universal recipient

f. universal donor

In the space provided, write the letter of the term or phrase that best completes each statement or best answers each question.

_____ 7. Antigens on the surface of red blood cells include
  a. A antigens.
  b. B antigens.
  c. Rh antigens.
  d. All of the above

_____ 8. Which of the following vessel walls has a thickness of only one cell layer?
  a. artery
  b. capillary
  c. vein
  d. arteriole

_____ 9. What occurs when the air pressure in the lungs is higher than in the atmosphere?
  a. inhalation
  b. the diaphragm contracts
  c. exhalation
  d. the rib cage moves up and out

_____ 10. The site(s) of gas exchange in the lungs is
  a. the bronchi.
  b. the alveoli.
  c. the bronchioles.
  d. All of the above

# The Body's Defense Systems

**Study the steps involved when a virus infects a body cell. Determine the order in which the steps take place. Write the number of each step in the space provided.**

_____ **1.** Interleukin-2 also activates B cells.

_____ **2.** Helper T cells bind to the viral antigen displayed by the macrophages, and macrophages release interleukin-1.

_____ **3.** B cells divide and develop into plasma cells, which release antibodies into the blood.

_____ **4.** Macrophages engulf the virus and display the viral antigens on their surfaces.

_____ **5.** Helper T cells activate cytotoxic T cells and B cells and release interleukin-2.

**In the space provided, write the letter of the term or phrase that best completes each statement or best answers each question.**

_____ **6.** The body's nonspecific defenses include which of the following mechanisms?
  **a.** the skin as a physical barrier to pathogens
  **b.** mucous membranes that produce mucus to trap pathogens
  **c.** an inflammatory response to suppress infection
  **d.** All of the above

_____ **7.** An example of an autoimmune disease is
  **a.** asthma.                                      **c.** botulism.
  **b.** rheumatoid arthritis.                         **d.** Lyme disease.

_____ **8.** The most common method of HIV transmission is through
  **a.** the air.                                      **c.** saliva and tears.
  **b.** sexual contact.                               **d.** mosquitoes and ticks.

_____ **9.** Antibodies are produced when the body is exposed to
  **a.** receptor proteins.
  **b.** macrophages.
  **c.** white blood cells.
  **d.** antigens.

_____ **10.** What is the four-step procedure used as a guide for identifying specific pathogens?
  **a.** pathogen isolation                            **c.** Jenner's postulates
  **b.** Koch's postulates                             **d.** vaccination

Assessment

# The Body's Defense Systems

**Study the steps involved when a virus infects a body cell. Determine the order in which the steps take place. Write the number of each step in the space provided.**

_____ 1. Interleukin-2 also activates B cells.

_____ 2. Helper T cells bind to the viral antigen displayed by the macrophages, and macrophages release interleukin-1.

_____ 3. B cells divide and develop into plasma cells, which release antibodies into the blood.

_____ 4. Macrophages engulf the virus and display the viral antigens on their surfaces.

_____ 5. Helper T cells activate cytotoxic T cells and B cells and release interleukin-2.

**In the space provided, write the letter of the term or phrase that best completes each statement or best answers each question.**

_____ 6. The body's nonspecific defenses include which of the following mechanisms?
   a. the skin as a physical barrier to pathogens
   b. mucous membranes that produce mucus to trap pathogens
   c. an inflammatory response to suppress infection
   d. All of the above

_____ 7. An example of an autoimmune disease is
   a. asthma.                          c. botulism.
   b. rheumatoid arthritis.            d. Lyme disease.

_____ 8. The most common method of HIV transmission is through
   a. the air.                         c. saliva and tears.
   b. sexual contact.                  d. mosquitoes and ticks.

_____ 9. Antibodies are produced when the body is exposed to
   a. receptor proteins.
   b. macrophages.
   c. white blood cells.
   d. antigens.

_____ 10. What is the four-step procedure used as a guide for identifying specific pathogens?
   a. pathogen isolation               c. Jenner's postulates
   b. Koch's postulates                d. vaccination

Name _____ Class _____ Date _____

# Digestive and Excretory Systems

**In the space provided, write the letter of the description that best matches the term or phrase.**

_____ **1.** carbohydrate

_____ **2.** lipid

_____ **3.** villus

_____ **4.** colon

_____ **5.** ureter

_____ **6.** urethra

**a.** tube through which urine exits the body

**b.** area of the digestive tract where most nutrients are absorbed

**c.** nutrient found in fruits, cereal grains, and vegetables

**d.** nutrient used to make cell membranes

**e.** area of the digestive tract where bacteria live and water is absorbed

**f.** tube that connects the kidney to the urinary bladder

**In the space provided, write the letter of the term or phrase that best completes each statement or best answers each question.**

_____ **7.** Digestion is
   **a.** the process of using the energy released from food to make ATP.
   **b.** the process of storing excess carbohydrates as glycogen.
   **c.** the process of making proteins from amino acids.
   **d.** the process of breaking down food into molecules the body can use.

_____ **8.** The small intestine receives secretions from which of the following?
   **a.** saliva                          **c.** pancreas
   **b.** stomach                      **d.** large intestine

_____ **9.** Within each Bowman's capsule is a fine network of capillaries called a
   **a.** glomerulus.                 **c.** collecting duct.
   **b.** renal tubule.                **d.** nephron.

_____ **10.** The renal tubules reabsorb all of the following molecules EXCEPT
   **a.** glucose.                       **c.** ions.
   **b.** ammonia.                     **d.** water.

Assessment

# Digestive and Excretory Systems

In the space provided, write the letter of the description that best matches the term or phrase.

_____ 1. carbohydrate

_____ 2. lipid

_____ 3. villus

_____ 4. colon

_____ 5. ureter

_____ 6. urethra

a. tube through which urine exits the body

b. area of the digestive tract where most nutrients are absorbed

c. nutrient found in fruits, cereal grains, and vegetables

d. nutrient used to make cell membranes

e. area of the digestive tract where bacteria live and water is absorbed

f. tube that connects the kidney to the urinary bladder

In the space provided, write the letter of the term or phrase that best completes each statement or best answers each question.

_____ 7. Digestion is
a. the process of using the energy released from food to make ATP
b. the process of storing excess carbohydrates as glycogen.
c. the process of making proteins from amino acids.
d. the process of breaking down food into molecules the body can use.

_____ 8. The small intestine receives secretions from which of the following?
a. saliva
b. stomach
c. pancreas
d. large intestine

_____ 9. Within each Bowman's capsule is a fine network of capillaries called a
a. glomerulus.
b. renal tubule.
c. collecting duct.
d. nephron.

_____ 10. The renal tubules reabsorb all of the following molecules EXCEPT
a. glucose.
b. ammonia.
c. ions.
d. water.

Assessment

# Nervous System and Sense Organs

**In the space provided, write the letter of the term or phrase that best completes each statement or best answers each question.**

_____ 1. The conduction of nerve impulses is faster in myelinated axons because
   **a.** neurotransmitter molecules are released in greater amounts.
   **b.** the myelin sheath covers the entire axon.
   **c.** nerve impulses "jump" from node to node as they move down the axon.
   **d.** the membrane potential does not change.

_____ 2. The resting potential of a neuron is usually which of the following?
   **a.** positive          **c.** neutral
   **b.** negative          **d.** Either a or b

_____ 3. The two main divisions of the nervous system are
   **a.** the autonomic nervous system and the somatic nervous system.
   **b.** the sympathetic division and the parasympathetic division.
   **c.** the central nervous system and the peripheral nervous system.
   **d.** the sensory division and the motor division.

_____ 4. Tars, produced from burning tobacco, do all of the following EXCEPT
   **a.** accumulate in the lungs and paralyze cilia.
   **b.** blacken lung tissue and decrease breathing ability.
   **c.** irritate mucous membranes in the mouth, nose, and throat.
   **d.** cause addiction to cigarettes.

_____ 5. Examples of psychoactive drugs include which of the following?
   **a.** caffeine          **c.** cocaine
   **b.** alcohol           **d.** All of the above

**In the space provided, write the letter of the description that best matches the term or phrase.**

_____ 6. detect movement, pressure, and tension                **a.** thermoreceptors
                                                                 **b.** pain receptors
_____ 7. respond to tissue damage                              **c.** mechanoreceptors
_____ 8. are stimulated by light                               **d.** photoreceptors
                                                                 **e.** chemoreceptors
_____ 9. located in the tongue and nose

_____10. detect changes in temperature

Assessment

# Nervous System and Sense Organs

**In the space provided, write the letter of the term or phrase that best completes each statement or best answers each question.**

_____ 1. The conduction of nerve impulses is faster in myelinated axons because
   a. neurotransmitter molecules are released in greater amounts.
   b. the myelin sheath covers the entire axon.
   c. nerve impulses "jump" from node to node as they move down the axon.
   d. the membrane potential does not change.

_____ 2. The resting potential of a neuron is usually which of the following?
   a. positive            c. neutral
   b. negative            d. Either a or b

_____ 3. The two main divisions of the nervous system are
   a. the autonomic nervous system and the somatic nervous system.
   b. the sympathetic division and the parasympathetic division.
   c. the central nervous system and the peripheral nervous system.
   d. the sensory division and the motor division.

_____ 4. Tars, produced from burning tobacco, do all of the following EXCEPT
   a. accumulate in the lungs and paralyze cilia.
   b. blacken lung tissue and decrease breathing ability.
   c. irritate mucous membranes in the mouth, nose, and throat.
   d. cause addiction to cigarettes.

_____ 5. Examples of psychoactive drugs include which of the following?
   a. caffeine            c. cocaine
   b. alcohol             d. All of the above

**In the space provided, write the letter of the description that best matches the term or phrase.**

_____ 6. detect movement, pressure, and tension

_____ 7. respond to tissue damage

_____ 8. are stimulated by light

_____ 9. located in the tongue and nose

_____ 10. detect changes in temperature

a. thermoreceptors

b. pain receptors

c. mechanoreceptors

d. photoreceptors

e. chemoreceptors

Name _____  Class _____  Date _____

# Endocrine System

**In the space provided, write the letter of the hormone the gland releases.**

_____ **1.** pituitary gland       **a.** parathyroid hormone

_____ **2.** thyroid gland       **b.** calcitonin

                                **c.** insulin

_____ **3.** parathyroid gland       **d.** epinephrine

_____ **4.** adrenal gland       **e.** antidiuretic hormone

_____ **5.** pancreas

**In the space provided, write the letter of the term or phrase that best completes each statement or answers each question.**

_____ **6.** "Releasing" and "release-inhibiting" hormones are secreted by the
     **a.** hypothalamus.          **c.** thyroid gland.
     **b.** pituitary gland.        **d.** pancreas.

_____ **7.** When a hormone-receptor complex enters the nucleus of a cell, it binds to
     **a.** DNA.                 **c.** ribosomes.
     **b.** enzymes.            **d.** RNA.

_____ **8.** An example of a second messenger is
     **a.** ATP.                  **c.** cyclic AMP.
     **b.** an enzyme.        **d.** glucagon.

_____ **9.** Steroid hormones are made from
     **a.** amino acids.
     **b.** enzymes.
     **c.** proteins.
     **d.** cholesterol.

_____ **10.** negative feedback : hormone ::
     **a.** temperature : thermostat
     **b.** accelerator : speed
     **c.** positive feedback : temperature
     **d.** lamp : light switch

# Endocrine System

**In the space provided, write the letter of the hormone the gland releases.**

_____ **1.** pituitary gland

_____ **2.** thyroid gland

_____ **3.** parathyroid gland

_____ **4.** adrenal gland

_____ **5.** pancreas

a. parathyroid hormone

b. calcitonin

c. insulin

d. epinephrine

e. antidiuretic hormone

**In the space provided, write the letter of the term or phrase that best completes each statement or answers each question.**

_____ **6.** "Releasing" and "release-inhibiting" hormones are secreted by the

a. hypothalamus.

b. pituitary gland.

c. thyroid gland.

d. pancreas.

_____ **7.** When a hormone-receptor complex enters the nucleus of a cell, it binds to

a. DNA.

b. enzymes.

c. ribosomes.

d. RNA.

_____ **8.** An example of a second messenger is

a. ATP.

b. an enzyme.

c. cyclic AMP.

d. glucagon.

_____ **9.** Steroid hormones are made from

a. amino acids.

b. enzymes.

c. proteins.

d. cholesterol.

_____ **10.** negative feedback : hormone ::

a. temperature : thermostat

b. accelerator : speed

c. positive feedback : temperature

d. lamp : light switch

Name _____ Class _____ Date _____

# Reproductive System

**In the space provided, write the letter of the description that best matches the term or phrase.**

_____ **1.** epididymis

_____ **2.** seminiferous tubules

_____ **3.** ovarian cycle

_____ **4.** menstrual cycle

_____ **5.** follicle

_____ **6.** chorion

**a.** cluster of cells that surrounds an immature egg cell and provides nutrients

**b.** membrane that interacts with the uterus to form the placenta

**c.** where sperm mature and become capable of moving

**d.** series of changes that prepare the uterus for a possible pregnancy each month

**e.** series of events in which an ovum is prepared and released

**f.** where sperm cells are produced

**In the space provided, write the letter of the term or phrase that best completes each statement or best answers each question.**

_____ **7.** After sperm mature, they move into the urethra by way of the
   **a.** penis.
   **b.** testes.
   **c.** bladder.
   **d.** vas deferens.

_____ **8.** At birth, a female's ovaries contain
   **a.** no egg cells.
   **b.** about 300–400 mature egg cells.
   **c.** about 400,000 immature egg cells.
   **d.** several sets of fertilized egg cells.

_____ **9.** The placenta and embryo are connected through the
   **a.** fallopian tube.
   **b.** umbilical cord.
   **c.** uterus.
   **d.** cervix.

_____ **10.** Aproximately one week after fertilization, the blastocyst burrows into the uterine lining during
   **a.** implantation.
   **b.** ovulation.
   **c.** cleavage.
   **d.** labor.

# Reproductive System

In the space provided, write the letter of the description that best matches the term or phrase.

_____ 1. epididymis

_____ 2. seminiferous tubules

_____ 3. ovarian cycle

_____ 4. menstrual cycle

_____ 5. follicle

_____ 6. chorion

a. cluster of cells that surrounds an immature egg cell and provides nutrients

b. membrane that interacts with the uterus to form the placenta

c. where sperm mature and become capable of moving

d. series of changes that prepare the uterus for a possible pregnancy each month

e. series of events in which an ovum is prepared and released

f. where sperm cells are produced

In the space provided, write the letter of the term or phrase that best completes each statement or best answers each question.

_____ 7. After sperm mature, they move into the urethra by way of the
a. penis.
b. testes.
c. bladder.
d. vas deferens.

_____ 8. At birth, a female's ovaries contain
a. no egg cells.
b. about 300–400 mature egg cells.
c. about 400,000 immature egg cells.
d. several sets of fertilized egg cells.

_____ 9. The placenta and embryo are connected through the
a. fallopian tube.
b. umbilical cord.
c. uterus.
d. cervix.

_____ 10. Aproximately one week after fertilization, the blastocyst burrows into the uterine lining during
a. implantation.
b. ovulation.
c. cleavage.
d. labor.

# Answer Key

## The Science of Life

| | |
|---|---|
| 1. e | 6. b |
| 2. c | 7. c |
| 3. a | 8. a |
| 4. b | 9. b |
| 5. d | 10. d |

## Chemistry of Life

| | |
|---|---|
| 1. b | 6. b |
| 2. c | 7. d |
| 3. d | 8. a |
| 4. a | 9. c |
| 5. a | 10. b |

## Biochemistry

| | |
|---|---|
| 1. b | 6. a |
| 2. c | 7. c |
| 3. d | 8. d |
| 4. a | 9. d |
| 5. e | 10. c |

## Cell Structure and Function

| | |
|---|---|
| 1. g | 6. a |
| 2. f | 7. e |
| 3. b | 8. c |
| 4. c | 9. d |
| 5. d | 10. b |

## Homeostasis and Cell Transport

| | |
|---|---|
| 1. c | 6. c |
| 2. d | 7. b |
| 3. b | 8. b |
| 4. a | 9. a |
| 5. c | 10. c |

## Photosynthesis

| | |
|---|---|
| 1. a | 6. a |
| 2. b | 7. c |
| 3. b | 8. b |
| 4. a | 9. c |
| 5. a | 10. d |

## Cellular Respiration

| | |
|---|---|
| 1. c | 6. a |
| 2. d | 7. c |
| 3. a | 8. b |
| 4. e | 9. d |
| 5. b | 10. c |

## Cell Reproduction

| | |
|---|---|
| 1. d | 6. c |
| 2. e | 7. b |
| 3. b | 8. c |
| 4. a | 9. c |
| 5. c | 10. b |

## Fundamentals of Genetics

| | |
|---|---|
| 1. b | 6. f |
| 2. e | 7. a |
| 3. d | 8. b |
| 4. c | 9. a |
| 5. a | 10. d |

## DNA, RNA, and Protein Synthesis

| | |
|---|---|
| 1. d | 6. e |
| 2. d | 7. b |
| 3. c | 8. a |
| 4. c | 9. d |
| 5. a | 10. c |

## Gene Expression

| | |
|---|---|
| 1. c | 6. a |
| 2. d | 7. b |
| 3. b | 8. e |
| 4. a | 9. d |
| 5. b | 10. c |

## Inheritance Patterns and Human Genetics

| | |
|---|---|
| 1. a | 6. c |
| 2. b | 7. f |
| 3. d | 8. e |
| 4. c | 9. d |
| 5. b | 10. a |

## Gene Technology

| | |
|---|---|
| 1. d | 6. g |
| 2. e | 7. b |
| 3. f | 8. a |
| 4. c | 9. d |
| 5. a | 10. a |

## History of Life

| | |
|---|---|
| 1. a | 6. b |
| 2. a | 7. d |
| 3. c | 8. e |
| 4. d | 9. a |
| 5. f | 10. c |

## Theory of Evolution

| | |
|---|---|
| 1. d | 6. b |
| 2. a | 7. c |
| 3. b | 8. a |
| 4. b | 9. e |
| 5. c | 10. d |

## Population Genetics and Speciation

| | |
|---|---|
| 1. c | 5. c |
| 2. b | 6. a |
| 3. c | 7. e |
| 4. b | 8. d |

## Classification of Organisms

| | |
|---|---|
| 1. b | 6. c |
| 2. d | 7. d |
| 3. b | 8. b |
| 4. a | 9. e |
| 5. a | 10. a |

## Introduction to Ecology

| | |
|---|---|
| 1. b | 6. d |
| 2. b | 7. a |
| 3. a | 8. e |
| 4. d | 9. b |
| 5. c | 10. c |

## Populations

| | |
|---|---|
| 1. c | 5. c |
| 2. a | 6. b |
| 3. d | 7. c |
| 4. a | 8. d |

## Community Ecology

| | |
|---|---|
| 1. c | 6. c |
| 2. d | 7. d |
| 3. a | 8. b |
| 4. c | 9. e |
| 5. b | 10. a |

## Ecosystems

| | |
|---|---|
| 1. c | 6. d |
| 2. b | 7. a |
| 3. d | 8. b |
| 4. d | 9. e |
| 5. a | 10. c |

## Humans and the Environment

| | |
|---|---|
| 1. f | 6. b |
| 2. d | 7. c |
| 3. a | 8. b |
| 4. e | 9. d |
| 5. c | 10. a |

## Bacteria

| | |
|---|---|
| 1. b | 6. f |
| 2. e | 7. a |
| 3. a | 8. a |
| 4. d | 9. d |
| 5. c | 10. b |

## Viruses

| | |
|---|---|
| 1. c | 6. e |
| 2. d | 7. d |
| 3. f | 8. b |
| 4. a | 9. d |
| 5. b | 10. c |

## Protists

| | |
|---|---|
| 1. e | 6. f |
| 2. d | 7. c |
| 3. b | 8. c |
| 4. g | 9. d |
| 5. a | 10. b |

## Fungi

| | |
|---|---|
| 1. b | 6. c |
| 2. a | 7. c |
| 3. c | 8. d |
| 4. b | 9. c |
| 5. a | 10. a |

## The Importance of Plants

1. d.
2. a
3. b
4. c
5. d
6. agriculture
7. Legumes
8. fertilizers
9. fungi
10. wind

## Plant Evolution and Classification

1. c          6. d
2. a          7. a
3. b          8. b
4. d          9. a
5. e          10. c

## Plant Structure and Function

1. c          6. c
2. d          7. a
3. b          8. b
4. a          9. b
5. d          10. a

## Plant Reproduction

1. a          6. a
2. d          7. c
3. c          8. a
4. b          9. a
5. e          10. c

## Plant Responses

1. c          6. f
2. e          7. a
3. a          8. c
4. b          9. d
5. d          10. c

## Introduction to Animals

1. a          6. f
2. d          7. b
3. c          8. e
4. c          9. a
5. d          10. c

## Sponges, Cnidarians, and Ctenophores

1. d          6. c
2. a          7. c
3. b          8. d
4. e          9. a
5. f          10. d

## Flatworms, Roundworms, and Rotifers

1. e          6. a
2. c          7. c
3. b          8. c
4. f          9. d
5. d          10. a

## Mollusks and Annelids

1. c          6. a
2. c          7. f
3. a          8. b
4. a          9. e
5. c          10. d

## Arthropods

1. d          6. b
2. f          7. d
3. a          8. b
4. c          9. a
5. e          10. c

## Insects

1. c          6. d
2. f          7. b
3. e          8. c
4. b          9. d
5. a          10. b

## Echinoderms and Invertebrate Chordates

1. f          6. b
2. a          7. b
3. d          8. b
4. e          9. d
5. c          10. d

## Fishes

| | |
|---|---|
| 1. e | 6. a |
| 2. d | 7. b |
| 3. a | 8. b |
| 4. b | 9. a |
| 5. c | 10. d |

## Amphibians

| | |
|---|---|
| 1. d | 6. c |
| 2. b | 7. d |
| 3. e | 8. a |
| 4. f | 9. a |
| 5. a | 10. c |

## Reptiles

| | |
|---|---|
| 1. a | 6. c |
| 2. e | 7. c |
| 3. c | 8. d |
| 4. b | 9. c |
| 5. d | 10. a |

## Birds

| | |
|---|---|
| 1. a | 6. c |
| 2. f | 7. d |
| 3. d | 8. c |
| 4. b | 9. b |
| 5. e | 10. a |

## Mammals

| | |
|---|---|
| 1. e | 6. b |
| 2. c | 7. b |
| 3. a | 8. c |
| 4. f | 9. b |
| 5. d | 10. c |

## Animal Behavior

| | |
|---|---|
| 1. d | 6. e |
| 2. f | 7. a |
| 3. c | 8. a |
| 4. b | 9. b |
| 5. g | 10. a |

## Skeletal, Muscular, and Integumentary Systems

| | |
|---|---|
| 1. b | 6. c |
| 2. d | 7. d |
| 3. a | 8. b |
| 4. e | 9. d |
| 5. c | 10. c |

## Circulatory and Respiratory Systems

| | |
|---|---|
| 1. d | 6. e |
| 2. a | 7. d |
| 3. c | 8. b |
| 4. b | 9. c |
| 5. f | 10. b |

## The Body's Defense Systems

| | |
|---|---|
| 1. 4 | 6. d |
| 2. 2 | 7. b |
| 3. 5 | 8. b |
| 4. 1 | 9. a |
| 5. 3 | 10. b |

## Digestive and Excretory Systems

| | |
|---|---|
| 1. c | 6. a |
| 2. d | 7. d |
| 3. b | 8. c |
| 4. e | 9. a |
| 5. f | 10. b |

## Nervous System and Sense Organs

| | |
|---|---|
| 1. c | 6. c |
| 2. b | 7. b |
| 3. c | 8. d |
| 4. d | 9. e |
| 5. d | 10. a |

## Endrocrine System

| | |
|---|---|
| 1. e | 6. a |
| 2. b | 7. a |
| 3. a | 8. c |
| 4. d | 9. d |
| 5. c | 10. b |

## Reproductive System

| | |
|---|---|
| 1. c | 6. b |
| 2. f | 7. d |
| 3. e | 8. c |
| 4. d | 9. b |
| 5. a | 10. a |